S0-AXX-177

Ancient Civilizations

Active Reading Note-Taking Guide

TEACHER EDITION

DOUGLAS FISHER, PH.D.
SAN DIEGO STATE UNIVERSITY

McGraw Hill Glencoe

New York, New York   Columbus, Ohio   Chicago, Illinois   Peoria, Illinois   Woodland Hills, California

ABOUT THE AUTHOR

Douglas Fisher, Ph.D., is a Professor in the Department of Teacher Education at San Diego State University. He is the recipient of an International Reading Association Celebrate Literacy Award as well as a Christa McAuliffe award for excellence in teacher education. He has published numerous articles on reading and literacy, differentiated instruction, and curriculum design as well as books, such as *Improving Adolescent Literacy: Strategies at Work* and *Responsive Curriculum Design in Secondary Schools: Meeting the Diverse Needs of Students.* He has taught a variety of courses in SDSU's teacher-credentialing program as well as graduate-level courses on English language development and literacy. He has also taught classes in English, writing, and literacy development to secondary school students.

 **Glencoe**

The *McGraw-Hill* Companies

Copyright © by The McGraw-Hill Companies, Inc. All rights reserved. Permission is granted to reproduce the material contained herein on the condition that such material be reproduced only for classroom use; be provided to students, teachers, and families without charge; and be used solely in conjunction with *Discovering Our Past: Ancient Civilizations.* Any other reproduction, for use or sale, is prohibited without written permission from the publisher.

Send all inquiries to:
Glencoe/McGraw-Hill
8787 Orion Place
Columbus, OH 43240-4027

ISBN 0-07-870307-7

Printed in the United States of America.

1 2 3 4 5 6 7 8 9 10 113 09 08 07 06 05

Table of Contents

Table of Contents

Dear Social Studies Student,

Can you believe it? The start of another school year is upon you. How exciting to be learning about different cultures, historical events, and unique places in your social studies class! I believe that this Active Reading Note-Taking Guide *will help you as you learn about your community, nation, and world.*

Note-Taking and Student Success

Did you know that the ability to take notes helps you become a better student? Research suggests that good notes help you become more successful on tests because the act of taking notes helps you remember and understand content. This *Active Reading Note-Taking Guide* is a tool that you can use to achieve this goal. I'd like to share some of the features of this *Active Reading Note-Taking Guide* with you before you begin your studies.

The Cornell Note-Taking System

First, you will notice that the pages in the *Active Reading Note-Taking Guide* are arranged in two columns, which will help you organize your thinking. This two-column design is based on the **Cornell Note-Taking System**, developed at Cornell University. The column on the left side of the page highlights the main ideas and vocabulary of the lesson. This column will help you find information and locate the references in your textbook quickly. You can also use this column to sketch drawings that further help you visually remember the lesson's information. In the column on the right side of the page, you will write detailed notes about the main ideas and vocabulary.

The notes you take in this column will help you focus on the important information in the lesson. As you become more comfortable using the **Cornell Note-Taking System**, you will see that it is an important tool that helps you organize information.

The Importance of Graphic Organizers

Second, there are many graphic organizers in this *Active Reading Note-Taking Guide*. Graphic organizers allow you to see the lesson's important information in a visual format. In addition, graphic organizers help you understand and summarize information, as well as remember the content.

Research-Based Vocabulary Development

Third, you will notice that vocabulary is introduced and practiced throughout the *Active Reading Note-Taking Guide*. When you know the meaning of the words used to discuss information, you are able to understand that information better. Also, you are more likely to be successful in school when you have vocabulary knowledge. When researchers study successful students, they find that as students acquire vocabulary knowledge, their ability to learn improves. The *Active Reading Note-Taking*

Guide focuses on learning words that are very specific to understanding the content of your textbook. It also highlights general academic words that you need to know so that you can understand any textbook. Learning new vocabulary words will help you succeed in school.

Writing Prompts and Note-Taking

Finally, there are a number of writing exercises included in this *Active Reading Note-Taking Guide*. Did you know that writing helps you to think more clearly? It's true. Writing is a useful tool that helps you know if you understand the information in your textbook. It helps you assess what you have learned.

You will see that many of the writing exercises require you to practice the skills of good readers. Good readers *make con-nections* between their lives and the text and *predict* what will happen next in the reading. They *question* the information and the author of the text, *clarify* information and ideas, and *visualize* what the text is saying. Good readers also *summarize* the information that is presented and *make inferences* or *draw conclusions* about the facts and ideas.

I wish you well as you begin another school year. This *Active Reading Note-Taking Guide* is designed to help you understand the information in your social studies class. The guide will be a valuable tool that will also provide you with skills you can use throughout your life.

I hope you have a successful school year.

Sincerely,

Douglas Fisher

To the Teacher

Dear Social Studies Teacher,

As you begin a new school year, one of the biggest challenges you will probably encounter is getting students to read their textbooks. Informational text can overwhelm students, leaving them less likely to read and more likely to become apathetic about learning. I believe that this Active Reading Note-Taking Guide *will help students use their textbooks more effectively as they learn about their community, nation, and world.*

Note-Taking and Student Success

There is considerable research evidence that addresses how students understand difficult concepts and content in school. Glencoe/McGraw-Hill has developed the *Active Reading Note-Taking Guide* for social studies students based upon that research. Evidence indicates that students need to know how to take notes, use graphic organizers, learn vocabulary, and develop their thinking skills by writing in order to achieve academic success.

Did you know that the ability to take and organize notes predicts how well students will do in school? Peverly, Brobst, Graham, and Shaw (2003) showed that when students use background knowledge and take notes, they are likely to perform well on tests. Pauk (1974) observed that note-taking was a critical skill for college success. Notes serve as an external storage function (meaning on the paper) that builds comprehension and content understanding (Ganske, 1981). This *Active Reading Note-Taking Guide* is a tool that students can use to achieve this goal. I would like to share some of the features of this *Active Reading Note-Taking Guide* with you before you begin teaching.

The Cornell Note-Taking System

First, you will notice that the pages in the *Active Reading Note-Taking Guide* are arranged in two columns, which will help students organize their thinking. This two-column design is based on the **Cornell Note-Taking System,** developed at Cornell University. Faber, Morris, and Lieberman (2000) found that the Cornell Note-Taking System improves comprehension and increases test scores.

The column on the left side of the page highlights the main ideas and vocabulary of the lesson. This column will help students find information and locate the references in their textbooks quickly. Students can also use this column to sketch drawings that help them visually remember the lesson's information. In the column on the right side of the page, students will write detailed notes about the main ideas and vocabulary. The notes they take in this column will help them focus on the important information in the lesson. As students become more comfortable using the Cornell Note-Taking System, they will see that it is an important tool that helps them organize information.

The Importance of Graphic Organizers

Second, there are many graphic organizers in this *Active Reading Note-Taking Guide.* Graphic organizers allow students to see the lesson's important information in a visual format. In addition, graphic organizers help students summarize information and remember the content. I hope that you will encourage students to use the graphic organizers because they will help them understand what they are reading.

Research-Based Vocabulary Development

Third, you will notice that vocabulary is introduced and practiced throughout the *Active Reading Note-Taking Guide*. When students know the meaning of the words used to discuss information, they are able to understand that information better. Also, students are more likely to be successful in school when they have vocabulary knowledge. When researchers study successful students, they find that as students acquire vocabulary knowledge, their ability to learn improves (Martino and Hoffman, 2002). The *Active Reading Note-Taking Guide* focuses on learning words that are very specific to understanding the content of the textbook. The guide also highlights general academic words that students need to know so that they can understand *any* textbook. These vocabulary words are based on the Academic Word List (AWL) developed by Averil Coxhead. The AWL includes the most common 570 words found in academic texts, excluding the 2,000 general English words such as *the, in,* and *that.* Research indicates that students who master the words on Coxhead's list score significantly higher on standardized tests.

Writing Prompts and Note-taking

Finally, there are a number of writing exercises included in this *Active Reading Note-Taking Guide*. Writing is a useful tool that helps students understand the information that is being presented. Writing helps them to assess what they have learned. You will see that many of the writing exercises require students to practice the skills of good readers. Good readers *make connections* between their lives and the text and *predict* what will happen next in the reading. They *question* the information and the author of the text, *clarify* information and ideas, and *visualize* what the text is saying. Good readers also *summarize* the information that is presented and *make inferences* or *draw conclusions* about the facts and ideas.

I wish you well as you begin another school year. This *Active Reading Note-Taking Guide* is designed to help students understand the information in your social studies class. The guide will be a valuable tool that will also provide students with skills that they can use throughout their lives.

I hope you have a successful school year.

Sincerely,

Douglas Fisher

References

Faber, J. E., Morris, J. D., and Lieberman, M. G. (2000). The effect of note taking on ninth grade students' comprehension. *Reading Psychology, 21,* 257–270.

Ganske, L. (1981). Note-taking: A significant and integral part of learning environments. *Educational Communication and Technology: A Journal of Theory, Research, and Development, 29,* 155–175.

Martino, N. L., and Hoffman, P. R. (2002). An investigation of reading and language abilities of college freshmen. *Journal of Research in Reading, 25,* 310–318.

Pauk, W. (1974). How to Study in College. Boston: Houghton Mifflin.

Peverly, S. T., Brobst, K. E., Graham, M., Shaw, R. (2003). College adults are not good at self-regulation: A study on the relationship of self-regulation, note taking, and test taking. *Journal of Educational Psychology, 95,* 335–346.

Van Leeuwe, J., and Aarnoutse, C. (1998). Relation between reading comprehension, vocabulary, reading pleasure, and reading frequency. *Educational Research and Evaluation, 4,* 143–166.

Chapter 1, Section 1
Early Humans

(Pages 122–131)

Main Idea

Setting a Purpose for Reading Think about these questions as you read:

- How did Paleolithic people adapt to their environment and use tools to help them survive?
- How did life change for people during the Neolithic Age?

Reading Strategy

As you read pages 123–131 in your textbook, complete this graphic organizer by filling in the causes and effects that explain how early humans adapted to their environment.

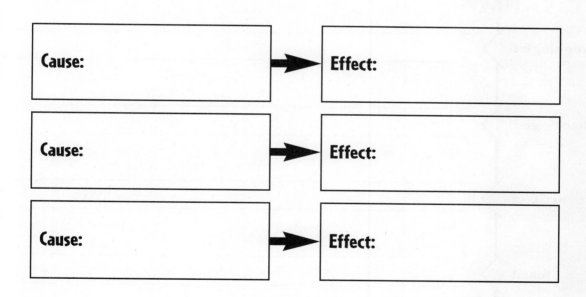

Cause:	→	Effect:
Cause:	→	Effect:
Cause:	→	Effect:

Copyright © by The McGraw-Hill Companies, Inc.

Early Humans *(pages 123–126)*

Visualizing

What would it be like to live in the Stone Age? As you read, list words and phrases that help you picture the life of early humans. Then write a paragraph describing a day in your life as a Paleolithic man or woman.

_____

_____

_____

_____

_____

Terms To Know

Define or describe the following terms from this lesson.

anthropologist

_____

_____

archaeologist

_____

_____

artifact

_____

_____

fossil

_____

_____

nomad

_____

_____

technology

_____

_____

Copyright © by The McGraw-Hill Companies, Inc.

Academic Vocabulary

Define this academic vocabulary word from this lesson.

task >

_____

_____

Sum It Up

What is the difference between a fossil and an artifact?

_____

_____

_____

_____

The Agricultural Revolution (pages 127–131)

Inferring

Why do some historians consider the farming revolution the most important event in human history? As you read, look for hints or ideas that support this idea. Record the hints you find in the web below.

The
Farming
Revolution

Copyright © by The McGraw-Hill Companies, Inc.

Key Points

Notes

Terms To Know

Define or describe the following terms from this lesson.

domesticate

_____

_____

_____

specialization

_____

_____

Places To Locate

Briefly describe the following place.

Jericho

_____

_____

Academic Vocabulary

Define this academic vocabulary word from this lesson.

revolution

_____

_____

Sum It Up

How did the Paleolithic and Neolithic Ages differ?

_____

_____

_____

_____

Copyright © by The McGraw-Hill Companies, Inc.

 **Key Points**

 **Notes**

 **Section Wrap-up**

*Now that you have read the section, write the answers to the questions that were included in **Setting a Purpose for Reading** at the beginning of the lesson.*

How did Paleolithic people adapt to their environment and use tools to help them survive?

_____

_____

_____

_____

_____

_____

How did life change for people during the Neolithic Age?

_____

_____

_____

_____

_____

_____

Read To Write Challenge

The agricultural revolution had benefits, but it also had drawbacks. On a separate sheet of paper, write a comparative essay describing both the advantages and disadvantages that emerged from the agricultural revolution.

Copyright © by The McGraw-Hill Companies, Inc.

Chapter 1, Section 2
Mesopotamian Civilization

(Pages 132–139)

Main Idea

Setting a Purpose for Reading Think about these questions as you read:
- Why did civilization in Mesopotamia begin in the valleys of the Tigris and Euphrates Rivers?
- How did the Sumerians contribute to later peoples?
- Why did the Sumerian city-states lose power?

Reading Strategy

As you read pages 133–139 in your textbook, complete this diagram to show how the first empire in Mesopotamia came about.

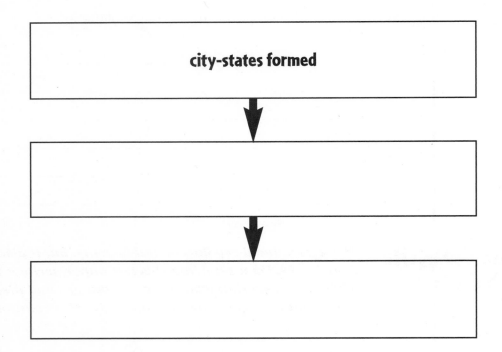

city-states formed

Copyright © by The McGraw-Hill Companies, Inc.

Mesopotamia's Civilization (pages 133–136)

Outlining *Complete this outline as you read.*

   I. Why Were River Valleys Important?

      A. _____

      B. _____

   II. The Rise of Sumer

      A. _____

      B. _____

   III. What Were City-States?

      A. _____

      B. _____

   IV. Gods and Rulers

      A. _____

      B. _____

   V. What Was Life Like in Sumer?

      A. _____

      B. _____

Terms To Know *Define or describe the following terms from this lesson.*

civilization > _____

_____

irrigation > _____

_____

Copyright © by The McGraw-Hill Companies, Inc.

city-state

artisan

Places To Locate

Briefly describe the following places.

Tigris River

Euphrates River

Mesopotamia

Sumer

Academic Vocabulary

Define this academic vocabulary word from this lesson.

complex

Copyright © by The McGraw-Hill Companies, Inc.

 Key Points

 Notes

Sum It Up

How did Mesopotamian control of the Tigris and Euphrates Rivers benefit their society?

_____

_____

_____

_____

A Skilled People (pages 136–137)

Drawing Conclusions

As you read, write three details about the Sumerians. Then write a general statement on the basis of these details.

1. _____

_____

2. _____

_____

3. _____

_____

General Statement > _____

_____

_____

_____

Copyright © by The McGraw-Hill Companies, Inc.

Key Points

Notes

Terms To Know

Define or describe the following terms from this lesson.

cuneiform

_____

_____

_____

scribe

_____

_____

Academic Vocabulary

Define this academic vocabulary word from this lesson.

consist

_____

_____

Terms To Review

Use each of these terms that you studied earlier in a sentence that reflects the term's meaning.

archaeologist
(Chapter 1, Section 1)

_____

_____

technology
(Chapter 1, Section 1)

_____

_____

Copyright © by The McGraw-Hill Companies, Inc.

 **Key Points**

 **Notes**

Sum It Up *How did the use of mathematics benefit the Sumerians?*

_____

_____

_____

_____

Sargon and Hammurabi *(page 139)*

Summarizing *As you read, complete the following sentences. Doing so will help you summarize the section.*

1. Sumeria was conquered by the _____. Their king,

_____, set up the world's first _____.

2. The Babylonian king _____ is best known for his collection

of _____. While some of his laws seem cruel, they were an

important step toward a fair system of _____.

Terms To Know *Define or describe the following term from this lesson.*

empire > _____

_____

Places To Locate *Briefly describe the following place.*

Babylon > _____

_____

Copyright © by The McGraw-Hill Companies, Inc.

 **Key Points**

 **Notes**

People To Meet

Explain why each of these people is important.

Sargon

_____

_____

_____

Hammurabi

_____

_____

Academic Vocabulary

Define this academic vocabulary word from this lesson.

code

_____

_____

Sum It Up

Why was Sargon's empire important?

_____

_____

_____

_____

Copyright © by The McGraw-Hill Companies, Inc.

Now that you have read the section, write the answers to the questions that were included in **Setting a Purpose for Reading** at the beginning of the lesson.

Why did civilization in Mesopotamia begin in the valleys of the Tigris and Euphrates Rivers?

_____

_____

_____

_____

How did the Sumerians contribute to later peoples?

_____

_____

_____

_____

_____

_____

_____

Why did the Sumerian city-states lose power?

_____

_____

_____

_____

Read To Write Challenge

Research Hammurabi's laws. Select three of his laws that you believe should be part of the U.S. system of justice. Then, on a separate sheet of paper, write a persuasive essay explaining why you believe these laws would benefit American society.

Copyright © by The McGraw-Hill Companies, Inc.

Chapter 1, Section 3
New Empires

(Pages 142–147)

Main Idea

Setting a Purpose for Reading Think about these questions as you read:
- How did Assyria build its vast empire?
- What major contributions did the Chaldean Empire make?

Reading Strategy

As you read pages 143–147 in your textbook, complete this diagram listing the similarities and differences between the Assyrian and Chaldean Empires.

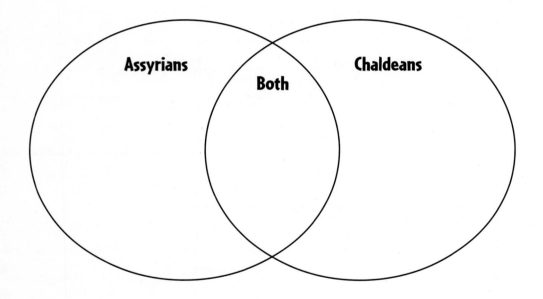

Assyrians

Both

Chaldeans

Copyright © by The McGraw-Hill Companies, Inc.

The Assyrians *(pages 143–144)*

Questioning

As you read, write three questions about the main ideas presented in this passage. After you have finished reading, write the answers to these questions.

1. _____
_____
_____

2. _____
_____
_____
_____

3. _____
_____
_____

Terms To Know

Define or describe the following term from this lesson.

province _____
_____

Places To Locate

Briefly describe the following places.

Assyria _____
_____

Persian Gulf _____
_____

Nineveh _____
_____

Copyright © by The McGraw-Hill Companies, Inc.

Academic Vocabulary

Define this academic vocabulary word from this lesson.

core >

_____

_____

Sum It Up

Why were the Assyrian soldiers considered brutal and cruel?

_____

_____

_____

_____

The Chaldeans _(pages 145–147)_

Determining the Main Idea

As you read, write the main idea of the passage. Review your statement when you have finished reading and revise as needed.

_____

_____

_____

_____

_____

_____

Copyright © by The McGraw-Hill Companies, Inc.

 **Key Points**

 **Notes**

Terms To Know

Define or describe the following terms from this lesson.

caravan

_____
_____
_____

astronomer

_____
_____

Places To Locate

Briefly describe the following place.

Hanging Gardens

_____
_____

People To Meet

Explain why this person is important.

Nebuchadnezzar

_____
_____
_____

Academic Vocabulary

Define these academic vocabulary words from this lesson.

interval

_____
_____
_____

route

_____
_____

Sum It Up

What were the Hanging Gardens of Babylon?

_____
_____
_____
_____
_____

Copyright © by The McGraw-Hill Companies, Inc.

Key Points

Notes

Now that you have read the section, write the answers to the questions that were included in **Setting a Purpose for Reading** *at the beginning of the lesson.*

How did Assyria build its vast empire?

_____

_____

_____

_____

_____

_____

What major contributions did the Chaldean Empire make?

_____

_____

_____

_____

_____

_____

Read To Write Challenge

The Assyrians are considered brutal and cruel, yet their empire was successful for almost 300 years. On a separate sheet of paper, write an **expository** *essay of three to four paragraphs explaining the positive features of Assyrian rule.*

Copyright © by The McGraw-Hill Companies, Inc.

Chapter 2, Section 1
The Nile Valley
(Pages 156–164)

Main Idea

Setting a Purpose for Reading Think about these questions as you read:
- Why did the early Egyptians settle in the Nile River valley?
- What role did the Nile River valley play in the development of the Egyptian civilization?
- How was early Egyptian society divided?

Reading Strategy

As you read pages 157–164 in your textbook, complete this diagram to describe Egyptian irrigation systems.

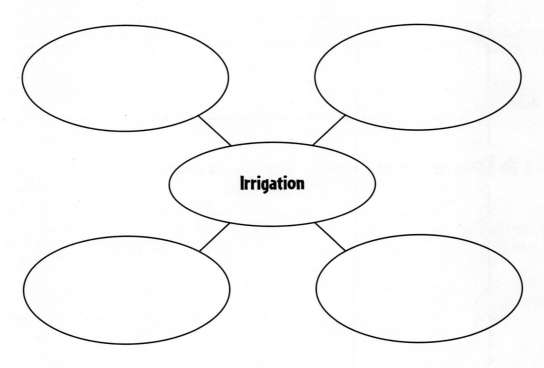

Copyright © by The McGraw-Hill Companies, Inc.

Settling the Nile (pages 157–158)

Determining the Main Idea

As you read, take notes describing the Nile and the area surrounding this great river. Use your notes to answer this question: How did the Nile and the surrounding area help protect Egypt?

_____

_____

_____

_____

Terms To Know

Define or describe the following terms from this lesson.

cataract

_____

_____

delta

_____

_____

Places To Locate

Briefly describe the following places.

Egypt

_____

_____

Nile River

_____

_____

Sahara

_____

_____

Copyright © by The McGraw-Hill Companies, Inc.

Academic Vocabulary

Define this academic vocabulary word from this lesson.

feature

_____

_____

Terms To Review

Use each of these terms that you studied earlier in a sentence that reflects the term's meaning.

civilization
(Chapter 1, Section 2)

_____

_____

city-state
(Chapter 1, Section 2)

_____

_____

Sum It Up

Describe the physical environment in Egypt.

_____

_____

_____

_____

The River People (pages 159–160)

Questioning

As you read, write three questions about the main ideas presented in the passage. After you have finished reading, write the answers to these questions.

1. _____

_____

_____

_____

Copyright © by The McGraw-Hill Companies, Inc.

2. _____
_____
_____
_____
_____

3. _____
_____
_____
_____
_____

Terms To Know

Define or describe the following terms from this lesson.

papyrus
_____
_____
_____

hieroglyphics
_____
_____

Academic Vocabulary

Define this academic vocabulary word from this lesson.

technology
_____
_____

Terms To Review

Use each of these terms that you studied earlier in a sentence that reflects the term's meaning.

irrigation
(Chapter 1, Section 2)
_____
_____

technology
(Chapter 1, Section 1)
_____
_____

Copyright © by The McGraw-Hill Companies, Inc.

 **Key Points**

 **Notes**

Sum It Up

How did living on the banks of the Nile help farmers?

_____

_____

_____

_____

A United Egypt *(pages 161–162)*

Drawing Conclusions

As you read, write three details about Narmer. Then write a general statement about Narmer's leadership on the basis of these details.

1. _____

_____

2. _____

_____

3. _____

_____

_____

General Statement

_____

_____

_____

Terms To Know

Define or describe the following term from this lesson.

_____

dynasty

_____

_____

Copyright © by The McGraw-Hill Companies, Inc.

Chapter 2, Section 1

 **Notes**

Sum It Up + *How were the kingdoms of Upper and Lower Egypt combined?*

_____

_____

_____

_____

Early Egyptian Life *(pages 163–164)*

Summarizing   *As you read, complete the following sentences. Doing so will help you summarize the section.*

1. The _____ was at the top of the early Egyptian social structure.

2. Egypt's upper class was made up of _____.

3. Egypt's middle class included people who _____.

4. _____ made up the largest group of early Egyptians.

5. _____ were at the bottom of the social structure in Egypt.

6. _____ had more rights in Egypt than in most other early civilizations.

Sum It Up + *How was Egyptian society organized?*

_____

_____

_____

_____

Copyright © by The McGraw-Hill Companies, Inc.

Section Wrap-up

Now that you have read the section, write the answers to the questions that were included in **Setting a Purpose for Reading** *at the beginning of the lesson.*

Why did the early Egyptians settle in the Nile River valley?

_____

_____

_____

_____

What role did the Nile River valley play in the development of the Egyptian civilization?

_____

_____

_____

_____

How was early Egyptian society divided?

_____

_____

_____

_____

Read To Write Challenge

Research hieroglyphics and the symbols used in this form of writing. On a separate sheet of paper, write an expository essay *describing the various types of hieroglyphic signs.*

Copyright © by The McGraw-Hill Companies, Inc.

Chapter 2, Section 2
Egypt's Old Kingdom

(Pages 165–170)

Main Idea

Setting a Purpose for Reading Think about these questions as you read:

- What were the main Egyptian beliefs about deities and the afterlife?
- Why did Egyptians build pyramids?

Reading Strategy

As you read pages 166–170 in your textbook, complete this graphic organizer to show the different religious beliefs in Egypt.

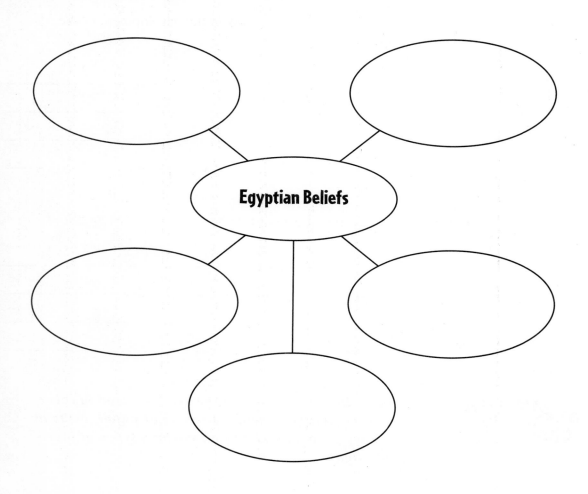

Copyright © by The McGraw-Hill Companies, Inc.

Old Kingdom Rulers *(page 166)*

Determining the Main Idea

As you read, write the main idea of the passage. Review your statement when you have finished reading and revise as needed.

_____
_____
_____

Terms To Know

Define or describe the following term from this lesson.

pharaoh

_____
_____

Academic Vocabulary

Define these academic vocabulary words from this lesson.

period

_____
_____

welfare

_____
_____

Sum It Up

Why did the pharaohs hold so much power?

_____
_____
_____
_____

Copyright © by The McGraw-Hill Companies, Inc.

Key Points

Notes

Egypt's Religion (pages 167–168)

Previewing

To preview this section, first skim the section. Then write a sentence or two explaining what you think you will be learning. After you have finished reading, revise your statements as necessary.

_____

_____

_____

_____

Terms To Know

Define or describe the following terms from this lesson.

deity

_____

_____

embalming

_____

_____

mummy

_____

_____

Sum It Up

Who were some of the main gods and goddesses of ancient Egypt?

_____

_____

_____

_____

Copyright © by The McGraw-Hill Companies, Inc.

The Pyramids *(pages 168–170)*

Inferring

Imagine standing at the foot of an ancient pyramid. What do these giant structures tell you about the Egyptian culture and people? As you read, take notes about the pyramids to help you answer this question.

_____

_____

_____

Terms To Know

Define or describe the following term from this lesson.

pyramid

_____

_____

People To Meet

Explain why this person is important.

King Khufu

_____

_____

Places To Locate

Briefly describe the following place.

Giza

_____

_____

Academic Vocabulary

Define these academic vocabulary words from this lesson.

structure

_____

_____

principle

_____

_____

Copyright © by The McGraw-Hill Companies, Inc.

 Key Points

 Notes

Sum It Up

What was the purpose of pyramids?

_____

_____

_____

Section Wrap-up

Now that you have read the section, write the answers to the questions that were included in **Setting a Purpose for Reading** *at the beginning of the lesson.*

What were the main Egyptian beliefs about deities and the afterlife?

_____

_____

_____

_____

_____

_____

Why did Egyptians build pyramids?

_____

_____

_____

_____

_____

Read To Write Challenge

Research the process of embalming. Then, on a separate sheet of paper, write two to three narrative paragraphs *sequencing the steps involved in embalming a pharaoh's body.*

Copyright © by The McGraw-Hill Companies, Inc.

Chapter 2, Section 3
The Egyptian Empire
(Pages 178–186)

Main Idea

Setting a Purpose for Reading Think about these questions as you read:
- What was life like during the Middle Kingdom?
- What important events happened during the New Kingdom?

Reading Strategy

As you read pages 179–186 in your textbook, complete this diagram showing the major accomplishments of Ramses II.

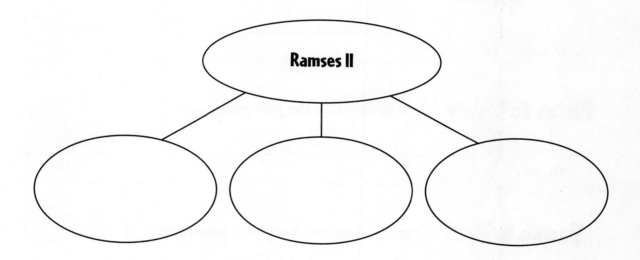

Copyright © by The McGraw-Hill Companies, Inc.

The Middle Kingdom (pages 179–180)

Skimming

The Middle Kingdom was a golden age for Egypt. Before you read, skim the passage. Make a note of any points that support this statement. Then, after you read, go back and fill in additional information about this golden age.

_____

_____

_____

_____

Terms To Know

Define or describe the following term from this lesson.

tribute

_____

_____

Places To Locate

Briefly describe the following place.

Thebes

_____

_____

People To Meet

Explain why this person is important.

Ahmose

_____

_____

Academic Vocabulary

Define this academic vocabulary word from this lesson.

restore

_____

_____

Copyright © by The McGraw-Hill Companies, Inc.

Sum It Up What advances in art were made during the Middle kingdom?

_____

_____

_____

_____

_____

The New Kingdom (pages 180–181)

Evaluating As you read, list the achievements of Hatshepsut and Thutmose III in the columns below. Then, based on the achievements you have listed, write a short paragraph evaluating the leadership of one of these rulers. Use specific examples from your list to support your opinion.

Hatshepsut	Thutmose III

Evaluation

_____

_____

Terms To Review Use this term that you studied earlier in a sentence that reflects the term's meaning.

pharaoh
(Chapter 2, Section 2)

_____

_____

Copyright © by The McGraw-Hill Companies, Inc.

Sum It Up Describe Egyptian trade during the rule of Hatshepsut.

_____

_____

_____

_____

Legacies of Two Pharaohs (pages 183–184)

Questioning *Before you read, skim the text. Then write three questions about the main ideas you find. After you have finished reading, write the answers to these questions.*

1. _____

_____

_____

_____

2. _____

_____

_____

_____

3. _____

_____

_____

_____

Copyright © by The McGraw-Hill Companies, Inc.

People To Meet

Explain why this person is important.

Akhenaton >

_____

_____

Academic Vocabulary

Define this academic vocabulary word from this lesson.

maintain >

_____

_____

Sum It Up

Why was the discovery of Tutankhamen's tomb so important?

_____

_____

_____

_____

The End of the New Kingdom *(pages 184–186)*

Sequencing

As you read, place the following events in the correct order by numbering them in the spaces provided.

1. _____ Groups from the eastern Mediterranean attack Egypt by sea.

2. _____ Egyptian armies regain lands in western Asia.

3. _____ Egypt is taken over by the Assyrians.

4. _____ Egypt is conquered by Libyans.

5. _____ Ramses II becomes pharaoh.

6. _____ Egypt is ruled by Kush.

7. _____ The temple at Karnak is built.

Copyright © by The McGraw-Hill Companies, Inc.

People To Meet

Explain why this person is important.

Ramses II

_____

_____

Academic Vocabulary

Define this academic vocabulary word from this lesson.

construct

_____

_____

Sum It Up

Why did Egyptian rulers lose control of their empire?

_____

_____

Section Wrap-up

Now that you have read the section, write the answers to the questions that were included in **Setting a Purpose for Reading** *at the beginning of the lesson.*

What was life like during the Middle Kingdom?

_____

_____

_____

What important events happened during the New Kingdom?

_____

_____

_____

Read To Write Challenge

Research the reign of Thutmose III. On a separate sheet of paper, write a descriptive paragraph *highlighting at least two "tricks" he used to conquer his enemies.*

Copyright © by The McGraw-Hill Companies, Inc.

Chapter 2, Section 4
The Civilization of Kush

(Pages 187–191)

Main Idea

Setting a Purpose for Reading Think about these questions as you read:
• Who were the Nubians and what were they known for?
• What was life like for the people of Kush?

Reading Strategy

As you read pages 188–191 in your textbook, complete this diagram to show the differences and similarities between Napata and Meroë.

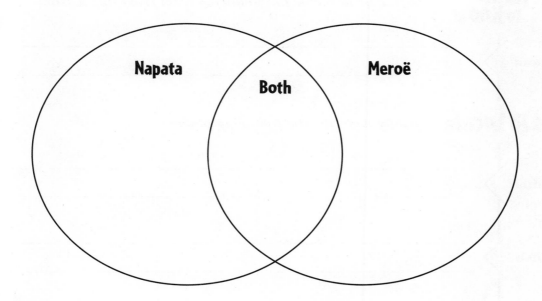

Napata

Both

Meroë

Copyright © by The McGraw-Hill Companies, Inc.

 **Key Points**

 **Notes**

Nubia *(pages 188–189)*

Determining the Main Idea

As you read, write the main idea of the passage. Review your statement when you have finished reading and revise as needed.

_____

_____

_____

_____

_____

Terms To Know

Define or describe the following term from this lesson.

savanna

_____

_____

Places To Locate

Briefly describe the following places.

Nubia

_____

_____

Kush

_____

_____

Kerma

_____

_____

Copyright © by The McGraw-Hill Companies, Inc.

Academic Vocabulary

Define this academic vocabulary word from this lesson.

collapse

_____

_____

Terms To Review

Use this term that you studied earlier in a sentence that reflects the term's meaning.

hieroglyphics
(Chapter 2, Section 2)

_____

_____

Sum It Up

Where was Kush located in relation to Egypt?

_____

_____

_____

_____

Copyright © by The McGraw-Hill Companies, Inc.

The Rise of Kush (pages 189–191)

Outlining
Complete this outline as you read.

I. The Importance of Iron

    A. _____

    B. _____

II. A New Capital

    A. _____

    B. _____

III. Building a Profitable Trade

    A. _____

    B. _____

Places To Locate
Briefly describe the following places.

Napata ⟩ _____

_____

Meroë ⟩ _____

_____

People To Meet
Explain why each of these people is important.

Kashta ⟩ _____

_____

Piye ⟩ _____

_____

Copyright © by The McGraw-Hill Companies, Inc.

Academic Vocabulary

Define this academic vocabulary word from this lesson.

decline

_____

_____

Terms To Review

Use each of these terms that you studied earlier in a sentence that reflects the term's meaning.

caravan
(Chapter 1, Section 3)

_____

_____

_____

dynasty
(Chapter 2, Section 1)

_____

_____

Sum It Up

How did Kush become a wealthy kingdom?

_____

_____

_____

_____

Copyright © by The McGraw-Hill Companies, Inc.

Chapter 2, Section 4

Now that you have read the section, write the answers to the questions that were included in **Setting a Purpose for Reading** *at the beginning of the lesson.*

Who were the Nubians and what were they known for?

_____

_____

_____

_____

_____

_____

What was life like for the people of Kush?

_____

_____

_____

_____

_____

_____

Read To Write Challenge

For centuries, Nubia was a land of legend. Even the ancient Greeks were fascinated by the mysterious land south of Egypt. Research how Europeans learned of the Nubian culture. On a separate sheet of paper, write a descriptive essay that includes quotes from the European explorer who first sighted the ruins of Meroë.

Copyright © by The McGraw-Hill Companies, Inc.

Chapter 3, Section 1
The First Israelites

(Pages 200–205)

Main Idea

Setting a Purpose for Reading Think about these questions as you read:

- What did the Israelites believe?
- Where was the Promised Land of the Israelites, and how did they return there?

Reading Strategy

As you read pages 201–205 in your textbook, complete this sequence chart to trace the movement of the Israelites.

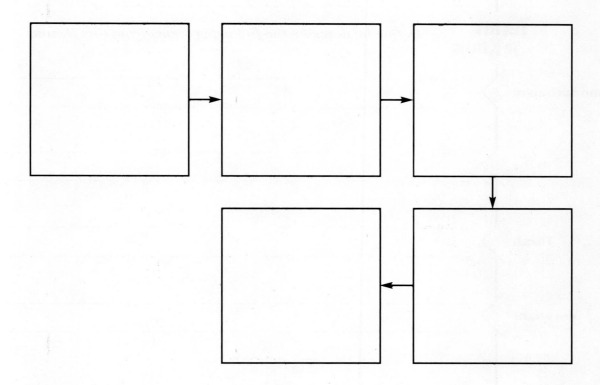

Copyright © by The McGraw-Hill Companies, Inc.

The Early Israelites (pages 201–203)

Copyright © by The McGraw-Hill Companies, Inc.

Connecting

As you read, consider how Judaism has influenced values in your culture today. Summarize your thoughts in a paragraph. Be sure to include specific ways that you see the values and beliefs of Judaism reflected in your world.

_____

_____

_____

_____

_____

_____

Terms To Know

Define or describe the following terms from this lesson.

monotheism

_____

_____

tribe

_____

_____

Torah

_____

_____

covenant

_____

_____

People To Meet

Explain why these people are important.

Abraham

_____
_____
_____

Jacob

_____
_____
_____

Moses

_____
_____
_____

Academic Vocabulary

Define these academic vocabulary words from this lesson.

focus

_____
_____
_____

occupy

_____
_____
_____

Terms To Review

Use this term that you studied earlier in a sentence that reflects the term's meaning.

pharaoh
(Chapter 2, Section 2)

_____
_____

Sum It Up

What is the Israelite belief in one god called?

_____
_____
_____
_____

Copyright © by The McGraw-Hill Companies, Inc.

Chapter 3, Section 1

The Promised Land *(pages 204–205)*

Responding

As you read the story of Joshua and Jericho, record your responses. What do you think about the story? What questions do you have? What do you learn about the Israelites and about Joshua? After reading the section, write a short paragraph summarizing your response to the story.

_____

_____

_____

_____

Terms To Know

Define or describe the following term from this lesson.

alphabet >

_____

_____

People To Meet

Explain why these people are important.

Deborah >

_____

_____

Phoenicians >

_____

_____

Academic Vocabulary

Define this academic vocabulary word from this lesson.

create >

_____

_____

Copyright © by The McGraw-Hill Companies, Inc.

Key Points | Notes

 Terms To Review

Use this term that you studied earlier in a sentence that reflects the term's meaning.

 **tribe**
(Chapter 3, Section 1)

_____

_____

Sum It Up

Who led the Israelites into Canaan, and what city did they conquer under his leadership?

_____

_____

Section Wrap-up

Now that you have read the section, write the answers to the questions that were included in **Setting a Purpose for Reading** *at the beginning of the lesson.*

What did the Israelites believe?

_____

_____

_____

Where was the Promised Land of the Israelites, and how did they return there?

_____

_____

_____

Read To Write Challenge

Research the family tree of Abraham. On a separate sheet of paper, write an expository essay *sequencing Abraham's known parents, brothers, and children.*

Copyright © by The McGraw-Hill Companies, Inc.

Chapter 3, Section 2
The Kingdom of Israel

(Pages 206–212)

Main Idea

Setting a Purpose for Reading Think about these questions as you read:
- Why did the Israelites choose to follow kings instead of judges?
- Who was King David and why was he important?
- Why were the Israelites conquered?

Reading Strategy

As you read pages 207–212 in your textbook, complete this chart to list the characteristics of Israel and Judah.

Location		
Capital City		
Date Conquered		
Conquered By		

Copyright © by The McGraw-Hill Companies, Inc.

 Notes

The Israelites Choose a King *(page 207)*

Determining the Main Idea

As you read, write the main idea of the passage. Review your statement when you have finished reading and revise as needed.

_____

_____

_____

_____

Terms To Know

Define or describe the following term from this lesson.

prophet

_____

_____

People To Meet

Explain why these people are important.

Philistines

_____

_____

Saul

_____

_____

David

_____

_____

Academic Vocabulary

Define this academic vocabulary word from this lesson.

instruct

_____

_____

Copyright © by The McGraw-Hill Companies, Inc.

Sum It Up

Why did the Israelites want a king?

_____

_____

_____

_____

David and Solomon *(pages 209–210)*

Summarizing

As you read, complete the following sentences. Doing so will help you summarize the section.

1. David defeated the giant Philistine named _____ with a

_____. As David won more victories, _____

became jealous and plotted to _____ David.

2. David took over the throne in about _____, when Saul and

his sons were _____ in battle.

3. David created an empire and established the capital of _____.

His son _____ built a great temple there.

4. When Solomon died, the 12 tribes broke into two nations:

_____ and _____.

Terms To Know

Define or describe the following terms from this lesson.

empire ⟩ _____

_____

Copyright © by The McGraw-Hill Companies, Inc.

tribute

_____
_____
_____

proverbs

_____
_____

Places To Locate

Briefly describe the following places.

Jerusalem

_____
_____
_____

Judah

_____
_____

Academic Vocabulary

Define this academic vocabulary word from this lesson.

symbol

_____
_____

Sum It Up

What did King David accomplish for Israel?

_____
_____
_____
_____

Copyright © by The McGraw-Hill Companies, Inc.

Key Points

Notes

A Troubled Time (pages 210–212)

Sequencing

As you read, place the following events in the correct order by numbering them in the spaces provided.

1. _____ The Egyptians conquer Judah.

2. _____ The Jews unite with the Egyptians to fight the Chaldeans.

3. _____ King Nebuchadnezzar captures Jerusalem.

4. _____ The Assyrians conquer Israel and scatter the 10 tribes.

5. _____ Nebuchadnezzar takes the Jews into captivity in Babylon.

6. _____ The Assyrians become known as Samaritans and eventually worship Israel's God.

7. _____ The Chaldeans conquer Egypt.

People To Meet

Explain why this person is important.

Nebuchadnezzar >

_____

_____

Sum It Up

Why did the Assyrians and Chaldeans want to control the land belonging to the Israelites?

_____

_____

_____

_____

Copyright © by The McGraw-Hill Companies, Inc.

Section Wrap-up

Now that you have read the section, write the answers to the questions that were included in **Setting a Purpose for Reading** *at the beginning of the lesson.*

Why did the Israelites choose to follow kings instead of judges?

_____

_____

_____

_____

Who was King David and why was he important?

_____

_____

_____

_____

Why were the Israelites conquered?

_____

_____

_____

_____

Read To Write Challenge

Research the major Hebrew prophets. On a separate sheet of paper, write a **descriptive essay** *comparing and contrasting at least three prophets and their teachings.*

Copyright © by The McGraw-Hill Companies, Inc.

Chapter 3, Section 3
The Growth of Judaism

(Pages 213–223)

Main Idea

Setting a Purpose for Reading Think about these questions as you read:
- How did Judaism grow in the period following the Jews' exile?
- Why did the Romans destroy the temple and exile the Jews?

Reading Strategy

As you read pages 214–223 in your textbook, complete this diagram to describe the Maccabees.

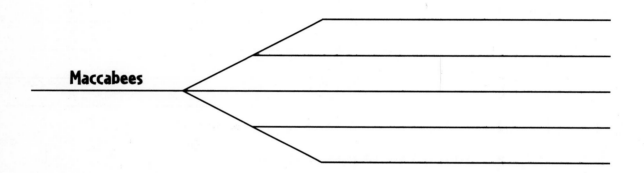

Copyright © by The McGraw-Hill Companies, Inc.

Exile and Return (pages 214–215)

Outlining

Complete this outline as you read.

I. Why Did Jews Return to Judah?

   A. _____

   B. _____

II. What Is in the Hebrew Bible?

   A. _____

   B. _____

III. The Jews Look to the Future

   A. _____

   B. _____

Terms To Know

Define or describe the following terms from this lesson.

exile >
_____
_____

Sabbath >
_____
_____

synagogue >
_____
_____

Places To Locate

Briefly describe the following place.

Babylon >
_____
_____

Copyright © by The McGraw-Hill Companies, Inc.

 Key Points

 Notes

Academic Vocabulary

Define this academic vocabulary word from this lesson.

series >

_____

_____

Terms To Review

Use this term that you studied earlier in a sentence that reflects the term's meaning.

scribe
(Chapter 1, Section 2) >

_____

_____

_____

Sum It Up

Who allowed the Jews to return to Judah?

_____

_____

_____

_____

The Jews and the Greeks (pages 215–216)

Questioning

As you read, write three questions about the main ideas presented in the text. After you have finished reading, write the answers to these questions.

1. _____

_____

_____

_____

Copyright © by The McGraw-Hill Companies, Inc.

2. _____

_____

_____

_____

3. _____

_____

_____

_____

Terms To Know

Define or describe the following term from this lesson.

Diaspora _____

_____

People To Meet

Explain why this person is important.

Judas Maccabeus _____

_____

Academic Vocabulary

Define these academic vocabulary words from this lesson.

version _____

_____

trace _____

_____

Copyright © by The McGraw-Hill Companies, Inc.

Key Points

Notes

Sum It Up

How did Alexander the Great affect the Israelites?

_____

_____

_____

_____

The Jewish Way of Life *(pages 217–218)*

Determining the Main Idea

As you read, complete the chart below to identify the main ideas from your reading.

The Jewish Way of Life

_____

_____

_____

_____

Copyright © by The McGraw-Hill Companies, Inc.

Sum It Up *Why were sons especially valued in Jewish society?*

_____

_____

_____

_____

The Jews and the Romans *(pages 220–223)*

Monitoring Comprehension *As you read, answer these questions to be sure you understand the main ideas of the section.*

1. What did Herod do as king?

_____

_____

_____

2. Why were the Jews unable to regain control over their Roman rulers?

_____

_____

_____

3. Who were the Pharisees?

_____

_____

_____

Copyright © by The McGraw-Hill Companies, Inc.

4. Who were the Sadducees?

_____

_____

_____

5. Who were the Essenes?

_____

_____

_____

6. What were the causes and results of the Jewish revolts?

_____

_____

_____

7. What role did rabbis play in Jewish society?

_____

_____

_____

_____

Terms To Know

Define or describe the following terms from this lesson.

messiah _____

_____

rabbi _____

_____

Copyright © by The McGraw-Hill Companies, Inc.

 **Key Points**

 **Notes**

People To Meet

Explain why each of these people is important.

Herod >

_____

_____

Zealots >

_____

_____

Johanan ben Zakkai >

_____

_____

Sum It Up

How did the Roman conquest affect the Jews?

_____

_____

_____

_____

Copyright © by The McGraw-Hill Companies, Inc.

Key Points

Notes

Section Wrap-up

*Now that you have read the section, write the answers to the questions that were included in **Setting a Purpose for Reading** at the beginning of the lesson.*

How did Judaism grow in the period following the Jews' exile?

_____

_____

_____

_____

_____

Why did the Romans destroy the temple and exile the Jews?

_____

_____

_____

_____

_____

Read To Write Challenge

*Research the Jewish festival of Purim. On a separate sheet of paper, write an **expository essay** explaining what Purim celebrates and what its four mitzvahs (requirements) include.*

Copyright © by The McGraw-Hill Companies, Inc.

Chapter 4, Section 1
India's First Civilization
(Pages 238–245)

Main Idea

Setting a Purpose for Reading Think about these questions as you read:
- What factors influenced the rise of India's first civilization?
- How did the Aryans change life in India?

Reading Strategy

As you read pages 239–245 in your textbook, complete this diagram to show how the Aryans changed India.

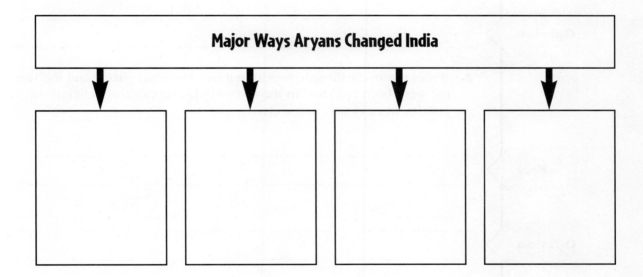

Copyright © by The McGraw-Hill Companies, Inc.

The Land of India *(pages 239–241)*

Evaluating

Look at the following statements from your reading. Evaluate each to determine which parts are facts and which parts are opinions.

1. "These ancient city dwellers had some surprising conveniences. Wells supplied water, and residents even had indoor bathrooms. Wastewater flowed to drains under the streets, running through pipes to pits outside the city walls. Houses also had garbage chutes connected to a bin in the street. It is likely the city government was well organized to be able to provide so many services."

Fact > _____

_____

_____

Opinion > _____

_____

2. "From the ruins, though, we can tell that the royal palace and the temple were both enclosed in the fortress. This reveals that religion and politics were closely connected."

Fact > _____

_____

_____

Opinion > _____

_____

Terms To Know

Define or describe the following terms from this lesson.

subcontinent > _____

_____

monsoon > _____

_____

Copyright © by The McGraw-Hill Companies, Inc.

Academic Vocabulary

Define this academic vocabulary word from this lesson.

similar

_____

_____

Terms To Review

Use this term that you studied earlier in a sentence that reflects the term's meaning.

archaeologist
(Chapter 1, Section 1)

_____

_____

Sum It Up

How did India's geography help early civilizations?

_____

_____

_____

_____

The Aryans Invade (pages 242–243)

Summarizing

As you read, write the facts you learn about cattle in the diagram below. You can use this diagram as a summary of your reading.

Aryan Cattle

Copyright © by The McGraw-Hill Companies, Inc.

Key Points

Notes

Terms To Know

Define or describe the following terms from this lesson.

Sanskrit

_____
_____
_____

raja

_____
_____

Academic Vocabulary

Define this academic vocabulary word from this lesson.

individual

_____
_____

Terms To Review

Use these terms that you studied earlier in a sentence that reflects the term's meaning.

nomad
(Chapter 1, Section 1)

_____
_____

tribe
(Chapter 3, Section 1)

_____
_____

Sum It Up

How did Aryan invasions change India?

_____
_____
_____
_____

Copyright © by The McGraw-Hill Companies, Inc.

Society in Ancient India (pages 243–245)

Connecting

The Aryans were light-skinned people and thought they were better than the dark-skinned people they had conquered.

1. Have you ever experienced discrimination because of how you looked or what you believed? How did it feel?

_____

_____

_____

_____

2. Where do you see discrimination in your world today? What effect do you think it has on society?

_____

_____

_____

_____

Terms To Know

Define or describe the following terms from this lesson.

caste 〉 _____

_____

guru 〉 _____

_____

Copyright © by The McGraw-Hill Companies, Inc.

Sum It Up

What were the five major groups in Indian society?

_____

_____

_____

_____

Section Wrap-up

Now that you have read the section, write the answers to the questions that were included in **Setting a Purpose for Reading** *at the beginning of the lesson.*

What factors influenced the rise of India's first civilization?

_____

_____

_____

_____

How did the Aryans change life in India?

_____

_____

_____

_____

Read To Write Challenge

In spite of the difficulties they faced, most Untouchables did not choose to convert to other religions or emigrate to other countries to escape their hard life. On a separate sheet of paper, write an **expository paragraph** *explaining the social pressures that might prevent a person from converting to a different religion.*

Copyright © by The McGraw-Hill Companies, Inc.

Chapter 4, Section 2
Hinduism and Buddhism

(Pages 246–253)

Main Idea

Setting a Purpose for Reading Think about these questions as you read:
- What is Hinduism?
- What is Buddhism?

Reading Strategy

As you read pages 247–253 in your textbook, complete the web diagram to identify the major beliefs of Hinduism.

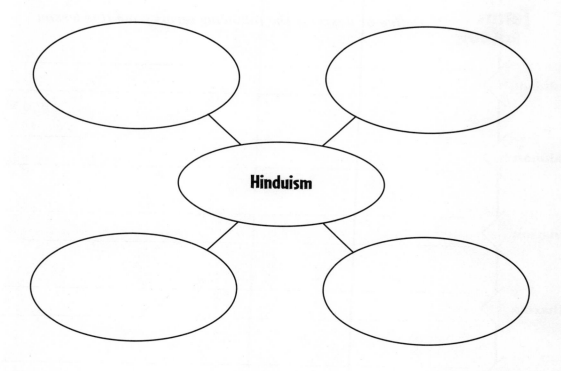

Copyright © by The McGraw-Hill Companies, Inc.

Key Points

 **Notes**

Hinduism *(pages 247–248)*

Synthesizing

You are a Hindu servant living in ancient India. Your friend who is not a Hindu has asked you to share information about your beliefs. Write a paragraph telling your friend what you believe and why your beliefs give you hope in life.

_____

_____

_____

_____

_____

Terms To Know

Define or describe the following terms from this lesson.

Hinduism

_____

_____

Brahman

_____

_____

reincarnation

_____

_____

dharma

_____

_____

karma

_____

_____

Academic Vocabulary

Define each of these academic vocabulary words from this lesson.

affect

_____

_____

Copyright © by The McGraw-Hill Companies, Inc.

require >

Terms To Review   Use this term that you studied earlier in a sentence that reflects the term's meaning.

Sanskrit
(Chapter 4, Section 1) >

Sum It Up   How did the beliefs of the Aryans influence Hinduism?

Buddhism (pages 249–253)

Scanning   Glance quickly over the reading to find answers to the following questions.

1. Who is the Buddha?

2. What is nirvana?

3. What are some of the key beliefs of Buddhism?

Copyright © by The McGraw-Hill Companies, Inc.

4. What are the different types of Buddhism?

_____

_____

5. Who is the Dalai Lama?

_____

_____

Terms To Know

Define or describe the following terms from this lesson.

Buddhism

_____

_____

nirvana

_____

_____

theocracy

_____

Academic Vocabulary

Define each of these academic vocabulary words from this lesson.

area

_____

_____

aware

_____

Sum It Up

How did Buddhism spread throughout Asia?

_____

_____

_____

Copyright © by The McGraw-Hill Companies, Inc.

Now that you have read the section, write the answers to the questions that were included in **Setting a Purpose for Reading** at the beginning of the lesson.

What is Hinduism?

_____

_____

_____

_____

_____

_____

What is Buddhism?

_____

_____

_____

_____

_____

_____

_____

Read To Write Challenge

Draw a Venn diagram that compares and contrasts the *Eightfold Path* with the *Ten Commandments*. Then, on a separate sheet of paper, use the information in your diagram to write an *expository essay explaining the similarities and differences between the two moral codes.*

Copyright © by The McGraw-Hill Companies, Inc.

Chapter 4, Section 3
India's First Empires

(Pages 259–267)

Main Idea

Setting a Purpose for Reading Think about these questions as you read:
- What were India's first great empires?
- What contributions did these empires make?

Reading Strategy

As you read pages 260–267 in your textbook, complete this chart to identify the important dates, capital city, and government of the Mauryan Empire.

	Mauryan Empire
Dates	
Capital City	
Government	

Copyright © by The McGraw-Hill Companies, Inc.

The Mauryan Dynasty *(pages 260–262)*

Inferring

Why do many historians think the Mauryan's greatest king was Asoka? Look for facts in your reading that support this statement. Write the facts you find in the diagram below.

King Asoka

Terms To Know

Define or describe these terms from this lesson.

dynasty

_____
_____
_____

stupa

_____
_____

Places To Locate

Briefly describe the following place.

Pataliputra

_____
_____

People To Meet

Explain why this person is important.

Chandragupta Maurya

_____
_____

Copyright © by The McGraw-Hill Companies, Inc.

Key Points

Notes

Sum It Up +

Why was Asoka an important ruler?

_____

_____

_____

_____

The Gupta Empire (page 264)

Determining the Main Idea

As you read, write the main idea of the passage. Review your statement when you have finished reading and revise as needed.

_____

_____

_____

Terms To Know

Define or describe the following term from this lesson.

pilgrim

_____

_____

Academic Vocabulary

Define this academic vocabulary word from this lesson.

dominate

_____

_____

Copyright © by The McGraw-Hill Companies, Inc.

Sum It Up

How did the Gupta empire become wealthy?

_____

_____

_____

_____

Indian Literature and Science (pages 265–267)

Reviewing

As you read, take notes in the chart below. You can use your notes to review the major contributions made by Indians in literature, mathematics, and science.

Literature	Math	Science

People To Meet

Explain why this person is important.

Kalidasa > _____

_____

Academic Vocabulary

Define this academic vocabulary word from this lesson.

concept > _____

_____

Copyright © by The McGraw-Hill Companies, Inc.

Chapter 4, Section 3

 **Key Points**

 **Notes**

Sum It Up

In what branches of science did ancient Indians make advances?

_____

_____

_____

Section Wrap-up

Now that you have read the section, write the answers to the questions that were included in **Setting a Purpose for Reading** *at the beginning of the lesson.*

What were India's first great empires?

_____

_____

_____

_____

_____

What contributions did these empires make?

_____

_____

_____

_____

_____

Read To Write Challenge

Research an ancient Indian fable. On a separate sheet of paper, write out the fable and then write a **descriptive** *paragraph* **summarizing** *the lesson that the story teaches.*

Copyright © by The McGraw-Hill Companies, Inc.

Chapter 5, Section 1
China's First Civilizations
(Pages 276–283)

Main Idea

Setting a Purpose for Reading Think about these questions as you read:
- What factors influenced the rise of China's first civilization?
- Why were China's early rulers so powerful?

Reading Strategy

As you read pages 277–283 in your textbook, complete this chart describing the characteristics of the Shang and Zhou dynasties.

	Shang Dynasty	Zhou Dynasty
Dates		
Leadership		
Accomplishments		

Copyright © by The McGraw-Hill Companies, Inc.

Key Points / Notes

China's Geography (pages 277–278)

Monitoring Comprehension

How did geography shape China's civilization? Complete the cause-and-effect diagram below to show the impact of geography. Completing the diagram will help you clarify your understanding.

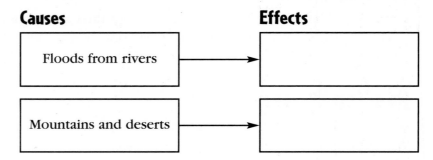

Causes

| Floods from rivers |

| Mountains and deserts |

Effects

Places To Locate

Briefly describe the following places.

Huang He

_____

_____

Chang Jiang

_____

_____

Sum It Up

Name two rivers important to early Chinese civilizations.

_____

_____

_____

_____

The Shang Dynasty (pages 278–281)

Outlining

Complete this outline as you read.

I. Who Were the Shang?

  A. _____

  B. _____

Copyright © by The McGraw-Hill Companies, Inc.

C. _____

D. _____

II. Spirits and Ancestors

   A. _____

   B. _____

III. Telling the Future

   A. _____

   B. _____

IV. The Chinese Language

   A. _____

   B. _____

V. Shang Artists

   A. _____

   B. _____

Terms To Know

Define or describe the following terms from this lesson.

dynasty _____

_____

aristocrat _____

_____

pictograph _____

_____

ideograph _____

_____

Copyright © by The McGraw-Hill Companies, Inc.

Places To Locate

Briefly describe the following place.

Anyang

_____

_____

Academic Vocabulary

Define these academic vocabulary words from this lesson.

recover

_____

_____

interpret

_____

_____

Terms To Review

Use each of these terms that you studied earlier in a sentence that reflects the term's meaning.

artifact
(Chapter 1, Section 1)

_____

_____

oracle
(Chapter 5, Section 1)

_____

_____

Sum It Up

What was the role of the Shang warlords?

_____

_____

_____

_____

Copyright © by The McGraw-Hill Companies, Inc.

The Zhou Dynasty (pages 281–283)

Questioning

As you read, write three questions about the main ideas presented in the text. After you have finished reading, write the answers to these questions.

1. _____
_____
_____
_____

2. _____
_____
_____
_____

3. _____
_____
_____
_____

Terms To Know

Define or describe the following terms from this lesson.

bureaucracy _____
_____

mandate _____
_____

Dao _____
_____

Copyright © by The McGraw-Hill Companies, Inc.

Key Points

Notes

People To Meet

Explain why this person is important.

Wu Wang

_____

_____

Academic Vocabulary

Define these academic vocabulary words from this lesson.

link

_____

_____

_____

item

_____

_____

Terms To Review

Use this term that you studied earlier in a sentence that reflects the term's meaning.

irrigation
(Chapter 1, Section 1)

_____

_____

Sum It Up

How did Zhou kings defend their right to rule?

_____

_____

_____

_____

Copyright © by The McGraw-Hill Companies, Inc.

 Section Wrap-up

Now that you have read the section, write the answers to the questions that were included in **Setting a Purpose for Reading** *at the beginning of the lesson.*

What factors influenced the rise of China's first civilization?

_____

_____

_____

_____

_____

_____

Why were China's early rulers so powerful?

_____

_____

_____

_____

_____

_____

Read To Write Challenge

Research Chinese pictographs and ideographs. On a separate sheet of paper, write an **expository** *paragraph explaining the difference between the two types of characters. Then write your name in Chinese.*

 Copyright © by The McGraw-Hill Companies, Inc.

Chapter 5, Section 2
Life in Ancient China

(Pages 284–291)

Main Idea

Setting a Purpose for Reading Think about these questions as you read:
• How was Chinese society organized?
• What were the three main Chinese philosophies of the time?

Reading Strategy

As you read pages 285–291 in your textbook, complete the pyramid diagram to show the social classes in ancient China from most important (top) to least important (bottom).

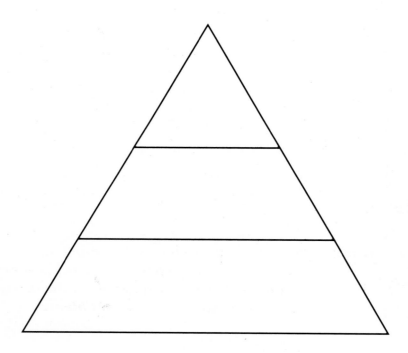

Copyright © by The McGraw-Hill Companies, Inc.

Life in Ancient China (pages 285–287)

Skimming

In Chinese society, farmers ranked above merchants. Before you read, skim the passage. Make a note of any points that support this statement. Then, after you read, go back and fill in additional information about the life of farmers in ancient China.

_____

_____

_____

_____

Terms To Know

Define or describe the following terms from this lesson.

social class

_____

_____

filial piety

_____

_____

Academic Vocabulary

Define this academic vocabulary word from this lesson.

convince

_____

_____

Sum It Up

Why did the amount of land owned by each aristocrat decrease over time?

_____

_____

_____

Copyright © by The McGraw-Hill Companies, Inc.

Chinese Thinkers (pages 287–291)

(pages 287–291)

Summarizing

As you read, summarize the main points of each of these Chinese philosophers in a few sentences.

Confucius	
Laozi	
Hanfeizi	

Terms To Know

Define or describe the following terms from this lesson.

Confucianism _____
_____

Daoism _____
_____

Legalism _____
_____

Academic Vocabulary

Define this academic vocabulary word from this lesson.

promote _____
_____

Copyright © by The McGraw-Hill Companies, Inc.

Sum It Up

Why did Hanfeizi believe that people needed laws and punishments?

_____

_____

_____

Section Wrap-up

Now that you have read the section, write the answers to the questions that were included in **Setting a Purpose for Reading** *at the beginning of the lesson.*

How was Chinese society organized?

_____

_____

_____

_____

What were the three main Chinese philosophies of the time?

_____

_____

_____

_____

Read To Write Challenge

Research The Analects of Confucius. *On a separate sheet of paper, write an* expository paragraph *summarizing in your own words one of the analects.*

Copyright © by The McGraw-Hill Companies, Inc.

Chapter 5, Section 3
The Qin and Han Dynasties

(Pages 294–303)

Main Idea

Setting a Purpose for Reading Think about these questions as you read:
- How did Qin Shihuangdi unify and defend China?
- What developments during the Han dynasty improved life for all Chinese?

Reading Strategy

As you read pages 295–303 in your textbook, complete this diagram to show the inventions of the Han dynasty and the resulting impact on society.

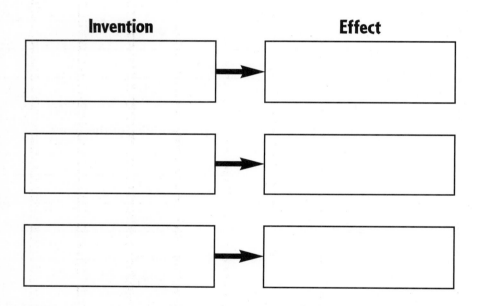

Invention	Effect

Copyright © by The McGraw-Hill Companies, Inc.

Emperor Qin Shihuangdi (pages 295–296)

Copyright © by The McGraw-Hill Companies, Inc.

Evaluating

List the accomplishments of Emperor Qin in the diagram below. Then evaluate his leadership. Write a brief paragraph to answer this question: Was he a good leader? Why or why not?

Qin's Accomplishments

Evaluation

_____
_____
_____

Academic Vocabulary

Define these academic vocabulary words from this lesson.

currency

_____
_____

civil

_____
_____

Sum It Up

Why did Qin face little opposition during most of his reign?

_____
_____
_____
_____

Monitoring Comprehension

As you read, answer these questions to be sure you understand the main ideas of the section.

1. What effect did the civil service examinations used by the Han dynasty have on the government?

_____

_____

2. Why did the aristocrats gain so much land?

_____

_____

3. What was the effect of the rudder?

_____

_____

Terms To Know

Define or describe the following term from this lesson.

acupuncture

_____

_____

Academic Vocabulary

Define these academic vocabulary words from this lesson.

founded

_____

_____

secure

_____

_____

Copyright © by The McGraw-Hill Companies, Inc.

Key Points

Terms To Review

Use each of these terms that you studied earlier in a sentence that reflects the term's meaning.

bureaucracy
(Chapter 5, Section 1)

_____
_____

aristocrats
(Chapter 5, Section 1)

_____
_____

Sum It Up

What inventions helped Chinese society during the Han dynasty?

_____
_____
_____
_____

The Silk Road (pages 300–302)

Determining the Main Idea

As you read, write the main idea of the passage. Review your statement when you have finished reading and revise as needed.

_____
_____
_____
_____
_____

Sum It Up

Why were mostly expensive goods carried on the Silk Road?

_____
_____
_____
_____

Copyright © by The McGraw-Hill Companies, Inc.

Major Changes in China (page 303)

Skimming

Quickly look over the entire selection to get a general idea about the reading. Then briefly describe the major changes that happened in China during this period.

_____

_____

_____

Sum It Up

What groups in China were first to adopt Buddhism?

_____

_____

Section Wrap-up

Now that you have read the section, write the answers to the questions that were included in **Setting a Purpose for Reading** *at the beginning of the lesson.*

How did Qin Shihuangdi unify and defend China?

_____

_____

_____

What developments during the Han dynasty improved life for all Chinese?

_____

_____

_____

Read To Write Challenge

Research the starting and ending points of the Silk Road. Imagine that you are a merchant carrying silk along the Silk Road. On a separate sheet of paper, write a narrative story *describing the people and dangers you encounter.*

Copyright © by The McGraw-Hill Companies, Inc.

Chapter 6, Section 1
The First Americans

(Pages 312–316)

Main Idea

Setting a Purpose for Reading Think about these questions as you read:

- How did the first people come to the Americas?
- What were the first American civilizations based on?

Reading Strategy

As you read pages 313–316 in your textbook, complete this chart to show the characteristics of the Olmec and Moche.

	Location	Dates	Lifestyle
Olmec			
Moche			

Copyright © by The McGraw-Hill Companies, Inc.

Farming in Mesoamerica (pages 313–314)

Analyzing

After you read, complete the chart below to identify the effects of the end of the Ice Age.

```
┌─────────┐
│ End of  │ ◁─────────────────────
│ Ice Age │      ─────────────────────
└─────────┘      ─────────────────────
```

Terms To Know

Define or describe the following term from this lesson.

glacier _____
_____

Places To Locate

Briefly describe the following place.

Mesoamerica _____
_____

Academic Vocabulary

Define these academic vocabulary words from this lesson.

expose _____
_____

estimate _____
_____

Sum It Up

How did the agricultural revolution begin in America?

_____
_____
_____
_____

Copyright © by The McGraw-Hill Companies, Inc.

Early American Civilizations *(pages 315–316)*

Drawing Conclusions

As you read, make a list of the important accomplishments of the first American civilizations. Then write a general statement that answers what these accomplishments tell you about these ancient peoples.

Civilization	Accomplishments
Olmec	
Maya	
Moche	

General Statement _____

_____

_____

_____

People To Meet

Explain why these people are important.

Olmec _____

_____

Maya _____

_____

Moche _____

_____

Places To Locate

Briefly describe the following place.

Teotihuacán _____

_____

Copyright © by The McGraw-Hill Companies, Inc.

Terms To Review

Use each of these terms that you studied earlier in a sentence that reflects the term's meaning.

empire
(Chapter 3, Section 2)

_____

_____

pyramid
(Chapter 2, Section 2)

_____

_____

Sum It Up

What was South America's first civilization? Where did it develop?

_____

_____

_____

Section Wrap-up

Now that you have read the section, write the answers to the questions that were included in **Setting a Purpose for Reading** *at the beginning of the lesson.*

How did the first people come to the Americas?

_____

_____

_____

What were the first American civilizations based on?

_____

_____

_____

Read To Write Challenge

Research the shamans, or holy men and women, of the Olmec people. On a separate sheet of paper, write an expository paragraph explaining the shamans' role in Olmec culture.

Copyright © by The McGraw-Hill Companies, Inc.

Chapter 6, Section 2
The Mayan People
(Pages 317–321)

Main Idea

Setting a Purpose for Reading Think about these questions as you read:
- What kind of civilization did the Maya create? Where did they live?
- What kind of society and culture did the Maya develop?

Reading Strategy

As you read pages 318–321 in your textbook, complete this web diagram to record Mayan achievements.

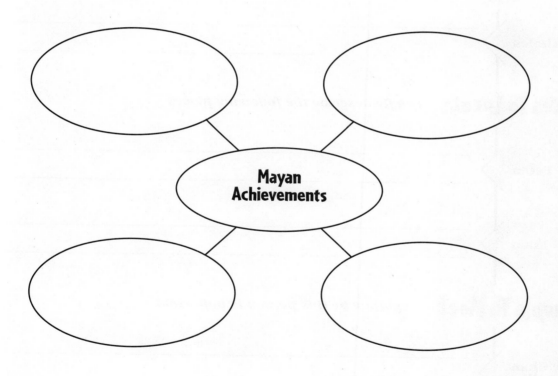

Mayan Achievements

Copyright © by The McGraw-Hill Companies, Inc.

The Mayan People *(page 318)*

Previewing

To preview this section, first skim the section, looking for headings and main ideas. Then write a sentence or two explaining what you think you will be learning. After you have finished reading, revise your statements as necessary.

_____

_____

_____

Terms To Know

Define or describe the following term from this lesson.

sinkholes

_____

_____

Places To Locate

Briefly describe the following places.

Petén

_____

_____

_____

Tikal

_____

_____

People To Meet

Explain why this person is important.

Jasaw Chan K'awiil I

_____

_____

Academic Vocabulary

Define this academic vocabulary word from this section.

access

_____

_____

Copyright © by The McGraw-Hill Companies, Inc.

Copyright © by The McGraw-Hill Companies, Inc.

Sum It Up

What was the main advantage of living in a tropical rain forest?

_____

_____

_____

Mayan Culture *(pages 320–321)*

Summarizing

As you read, complete the following sentences. Doing so will help you summarize the section.

1. Mayan rulers claimed to be _____ who were descended from the _____. The Maya sacrificed _____ and built a huge _____ to honor their gods.

2. Mayan priests studied the _____ closely to reveal the plans of the gods. They developed a _____ _____ to keep track of the heavenly movements. They also invented a written language using _____.

3. The Mayan civilization was at its peak around the year A.D. _____, but by the A.D. _____, their cities were deserted.

Terms To Know

Define or describe the following term from this lesson.

alliance _____

_____

Key Points

Notes

Academic Vocabulary

Define this academic vocabulary word from this lesson.

predict >

_____

_____

Sum It Up

How did the Maya treat enslaved people?

_____

_____

_____

Section Wrap-up

*Now that you have read the section, write the answers to the questions that were included in **Setting a Purpose for Reading** at the beginning of the lesson.*

What kind of civilization did the Maya create? Where did they live?

_____

_____

_____

What kind of society and culture did the Maya develop?

_____

_____

_____

Read To Write Challenge

Research the Popol Vuh, *or creation myth of the Maya. On a separate sheet of paper, write an expository essay summarizing how the Maya believed humans were created.*

Copyright © by The McGraw-Hill Companies, Inc.

Chapter 7, Section 1
The Early Greeks

(Pages 336–343)

Main Idea

Setting a Purpose for Reading Think about these questions as you read:
- How did early Greek kingdoms develop?
- What ideas developed in Greek city-states?

Reading Strategy

As you read pages 337–343 in your textbook, complete this diagram by filling in details about the polis.

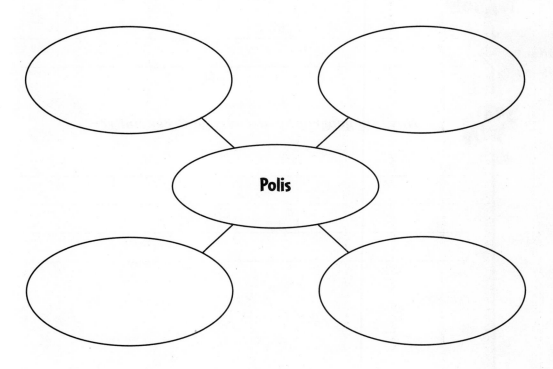

Copyright © by The McGraw-Hill Companies, Inc.

Notes

The Geography of Greece *(page 337)*

Visualizing

As you read, list words and phrases that help you picture the land of Greece. Now imagine you are a Greek sailor or trader. Write a paragraph in your own words about what you see around you.

_____

_____

_____

_____

Terms To Know

Define or describe the following key term from this lesson.

> peninsula

_____

_____

Sum It Up

How did geography discourage Greek unity?

_____

_____

_____

_____

Copyright © by The McGraw-Hill Companies, Inc.

The Minoans *(page 338)*

Questioning

Before you read, skim the section and write three questions about the main ideas you find. After you have finished reading, write the answers to these questions.

1. _____
   _____
   _____
   _____

2. _____
   _____
   _____
   _____

3. _____
   _____
   _____
   _____

Academic Vocabulary

Define this academic vocabulary word from this lesson.

region > _____
          _____

Places To Locate

Briefly describe the following place.

Crete > _____
          _____

Copyright © by The McGraw-Hill Companies, Inc.

Terms To Review

Use each of these terms that you studied earlier in a sentence that reflects the term's meaning.

archaeologist
(Chapter 1, Section 1)

_____
_____
_____

civilization
(Chapter 1, Section 2)

_____
_____

Sum It Up

How did the Minoans become a trading civilization?

_____
_____
_____
_____
_____

The First Greek Kingdoms (pages 339–340)

Outlining

Complete this outline as you read.

I. What Were Mycenaean Kingdoms Like?

    A. _____

    B. _____

II. Power From Trade and War

    A. _____

    B. _____

III. What Was the Dark Age?

    A. _____

    B. _____

Copyright © by The McGraw-Hill Companies, Inc.

 **Key Points**

 **Notes**

People To Meet

Explain why this person is important.

Agamemnon
_____
_____

Places To Locate

Briefly describe the following places.

Mycenae
_____
_____

Peloponnesus
_____
_____

Academic Vocabulary

Define these academic vocabulary words from this lesson.

culture
_____
_____

overseas
_____
_____

Terms To Review

Use this term that you studied earlier in a sentence that reflects the term's meaning.

artisan
(Chapter 1, Section 2)
_____
_____

Copyright © by The McGraw-Hill Companies, Inc.

Sum It Up

Why were the Mycenaeans able to become a major power in the Mediterranean region?

_____

_____

_____

_____

The Polis (pages 341–342)

Previewing

To preview this section, first skim the section, looking for headings and main ideas. Then write a sentence or two explaining what you think you will be learning. After you have finished reading, revise your statements as necessary.

_____

_____

_____

Terms To Know

Define or describe the following terms from this lesson.

polis

_____

_____

agora

_____

Academic Vocabulary

Define this academic vocabulary word from this lesson.

community

_____

Copyright © by The McGraw-Hill Companies, Inc.

 Key Points

 Notes

Terms To Review

Use this term that you studied earlier in a sentence that reflects the term's meaning.

city-state
(Chapter 1, Section 2)

_____

_____

Sum It Up

How did citizenship make the Greeks different from other ancient peoples?

_____

_____

_____

_____

A Move to Colonize _(page 343)_

Determining the Main Idea

As you read, write the main idea of the passage. Review your statement when you have finished reading and revise as needed.

_____

_____

_____

_____

Terms To Know

Define or describe the following term from this lesson.

colony

_____

_____

Copyright © by The McGraw-Hill Companies, Inc.

Key Points

Notes

Sum It Up +

How did the founding of new Greek colonies affect industry?

_____

_____

_____

_____

Section Wrap-up

Now that you have read the section, write the answers to the questions that were included in **Setting a Purpose for Reading** *at the beginning of the lesson.*

How did early Greek kingdoms develop?

_____

_____

_____

_____

_____

What ideas developed in Greek city-states?

_____

_____

_____

_____

_____

Read To Write Challenge

Use library resources or the Internet to research the labyrinth at the palace of Knossos. On a separate sheet of paper, write a narrative essay *summarizing the legend of Theseus and the Minotaur in your own words.*

Copyright © by The McGraw-Hill Companies, Inc.

Chapter 7, Section 2
Sparta and Athens
(Pages 344–350)

Main Idea

Setting a Purpose for Reading Think about these questions as you read:
• Why did Spartans conquer and control groups of people?
• How were the people of Athens different from the people of Sparta?

Reading Strategy

As you read pages 345–350 in your textbook, complete this graphic organizer comparing and contrasting life in Sparta and Athens.

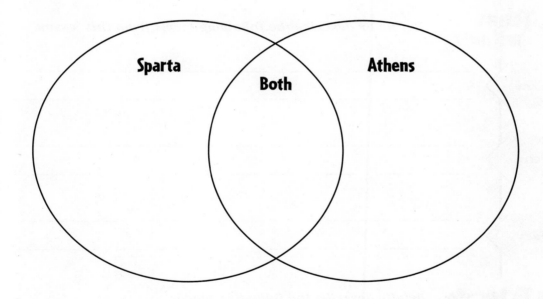

Sparta   Both   Athens

Copyright © by The McGraw-Hill Companies, Inc.

Tyranny in the City-States (pages 345–346)

Summarizing

As you read, complete the following sentences. Doing so will help you summarize the section.

1. _____, _____, and _____ all wanted a part in Greek government. Their unhappiness led to the rise of _____, men who took power by force. These tyrants took power away from the _____.

2. Most Greeks wanted all _____ to be a part of the government. So most city-states became either _____ or _____.

Terms To Know

Define or describe the following terms from this lesson.

tyrant _____
_____

oligarchy _____
_____

democracy _____
_____

Places To Locate

Briefly describe the following places.

Sparta _____
_____

Athens _____
_____

Copyright © by The McGraw-Hill Companies, Inc.

Sum It Up + Why were tyrants popular in the city-states?

_____

_____

_____

_____

Sparta (pages 346–347)

Drawing Conclusions   As you read, write three details about the Spartans. Then write a general statement or conclusion about the Spartans based on these details.

1. _____

_____

2. _____

_____

3. _____

_____

_____

General Statement > _____

_____

_____

Terms To Know   Define or describe the following term from this lesson.

helots > _____

_____

Copyright © by The McGraw-Hill Companies, Inc.

Academic Vocabulary

Define this academic vocabulary word from this lesson.

enforce >

_____

_____

Sum It Up +

Why did the Spartans focus on military training?

_____

_____

Athens (pages 348–350)

Connecting

What do you know about your state and national government? Think about things you have seen or read in the news. As you read, compare your state and national government with the democracy of Athens. Summarize your thoughts in a paragraph. Be sure to address the similarities and differences that you see.

_____

_____

_____

_____

Academic Vocabulary

Define this academic vocabulary word from this lesson.

participate >

_____

_____

People To Meet

Explain why each of these people is important.

Solon >

_____

_____

Copyright © by The McGraw-Hill Companies, Inc.

 **Key Points**

 **Notes**

Peisistratus _____
_____
_____

Cleisthenes _____
_____

Sum It Up + *How did Cleisthenes build a democracy in Athens?*

_____
_____

Section Wrap-up *Now that you have read the section, write the answers to the questions that were included in* **Setting a Purpose for Reading** *at the beginning of the lesson.*

Why did Spartans conquer and control groups of people?

_____
_____
_____

How were the people of Athens different from the people of Sparta?

_____
_____
_____

Read To Write Challenge *Review the lifestyles of the Spartans and Athenians. Then, on a separate sheet of paper, write a persuasive essay trying to convince one culture to become more like the other.*

Copyright © by The McGraw-Hill Companies, Inc.

Chapter 7, Section 3
Persia Attacks the Greeks

(Pages 351–357)

Main Idea

Setting a Purpose for Reading Think about these questions as you read:
- How did the Persian Empire bring together such a wide area?
- What role did Athens and Sparta play in defeating the Persians?

Reading Strategy

As you read pages 352–357 in your textbook, complete this graphic organizer listing the accomplishments of Cyrus, Darius, and Xerxes.

Ruler	Accomplishments
Cyrus	
Darius	
Xerxes	

Copyright © by The McGraw-Hill Companies, Inc.

The Persian Empire *(pages 352–353)*

Outlining
Complete this outline as you read.

I. The Rise of the Persian Empire

    A. _____

    B. _____

II. What Was Persian Government Like?

    A. _____

    B. _____

III. The Persian Religion

    A. _____

    B. _____

Terms To Know
Define or describe the following terms from this lesson.

satrapies
_____
_____

satrap
_____
_____

Zoroastrianism
_____
_____

People To Meet
Explain why this person is important.

Cyrus the Great
_____
_____

Copyright © by The McGraw-Hill Companies, Inc.

 **Key Points**

 **Notes**

Academic Vocabulary

Define this academic vocabulary word from this lesson.

vision

_____

_____

Terms To Review

Use each of these terms that you studied earlier in a sentence that reflects the term's meaning.

nomad
(Chapter 1, Section 1)

_____

_____

_____

empire
(Chapter 3, Section 2)

_____

_____

Sum It Up

What did Darius do to make his government work better?

_____

_____

_____

_____

Copyright © by The McGraw-Hill Companies, Inc.

The Persian Wars (pages 354–357)

Sequencing   *As you read, number the following events in the correct order.*

a. _____ Greek army crushed the Persian army at Plataea.

b. _____ Persian fleet landed 20,000 soldiers on the plain of Marathon.

c. _____ Athenian army helped the Greeks in Asia Minor rebel against Persian rulers.

d. _____ Xerxes launches invasion of Greece.

e. _____ Alexander invades the Persian Empire.

f. _____ Darius dies.

Places To Locate   *Briefly describe the following places.*

Marathon _____
_____

Thermopylae _____
_____

Salamis _____
_____

Plataea _____
_____

People To Meet   *Explain why each of these people is important.*

Xerxes _____
_____

Themistocles _____
_____

Copyright © by The McGraw-Hill Companies, Inc.

Key Points

Notes

Academic Vocabulary

Define this academic vocabulary word from this lesson.

internal

_____

_____

Sum It Up

What led to the Persian Wars?

_____

_____

_____

Section Wrap-up

Now that you have read the section, write the answers to the questions that were included in **Setting a Purpose for Reading** *at the beginning of the lesson.*

How did the Persian Empire bring together such a wide area?

_____

_____

_____

_____

What role did Athens and Sparta play in defeating the Persians?

_____

_____

_____

_____

Read To Write Challenge

Research King Leonidas of Sparta and his stand against the Persian army at Thermopylae. On a separate sheet of paper, write a narrative paragraph *telling the story of what happened.*

Copyright © by The McGraw-Hill Companies, Inc.

Chapter 7, Section 4
The Age of Pericles

(Pages 358–367)

Main Idea

Setting a Purpose for Reading Think about these questions as you read:
- How did Athens change under the rule of Pericles?
- What happened when Sparta and Athens went to war for control of Greece?

Reading Strategy

As you read pages 359–367 in your textbook, create a circle graph showing how many citizens, foreigners, and enslaved people lived in Athens in the 400s B.C.

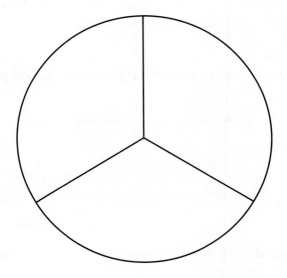

Copyright © by The McGraw-Hill Companies, Inc.

The Athenian Empire (pages 359–360)

Evaluating

What do you think makes a leader great? Think of leaders you have known or heard about. Then, as you read, list the achievements of Pericles. Based on the achievements you have listed, write a paragraph evaluating his leadership. Use specific examples from your list to support your opinion.

_____

_____

_____

_____

_____

_____

_____

Terms To Know

Define or describe the following terms from this lesson.

direct democracy

_____

_____

representative democracy

_____

_____

philosophers

_____

_____

Places To Locate

Briefly describe the following place.

Delos

_____

_____

Copyright © by The McGraw-Hill Companies, Inc.

 **Key Points**

 **Notes**

People To Meet

Explain why this person is important.

Pericles

_____

_____

Academic Vocabulary

Define this academic vocabulary word from this lesson.

behalf

_____

_____

Sum It Up

What is the difference between a direct democracy and a representative democracy?

_____

_____

_____

_____

Daily Life in Athens (pages 362–363)

Questioning

What was life like in Athens? Before you read, skim the reading to identify main ideas. Then write three questions you think your reading will answer. After you have finished reading, write the answers to these questions.

1. _____

_____

_____

_____

Copyright © by The McGraw-Hill Companies, Inc.

2. _____

_____

_____

_____

3. _____

_____

_____

_____

People To Meet

Explain why this person is important.

Aspasia

_____

_____

Academic Vocabulary

Define this academic vocabulary word from this lesson.

economy

_____

_____

Sum It Up

How did Athenian men and women spend their time?

_____

_____

_____

_____

Copyright © by The McGraw-Hill Companies, Inc.

The Peloponnesian War *(pages 364–367)*

Predicting

Before you read, based on what you know about Sparta and Athens, predict who you think will win the war. Support your prediction with facts from your reading. After you read, write a paragraph about your reaction to the actual outcome.

_____

_____

_____

_____

_____

_____

_____

_____

_____

_____

_____

_____

_____

_____

_____

Academic Vocabulary

Define this academic vocabulary word from this lesson.

framework >

_____

_____

Copyright © by The McGraw-Hill Companies, Inc.

Chapter 7, Section 4

Key Points

Notes

Sum It Up

What effects did the Peloponnesian War have on Greece?

_____

_____

_____

_____

Section Wrap-up

Now that you have read the section, write the answers to the questions that were included in **Setting a Purpose for Reading** *at the beginning of the lesson.*

How did Athens change under the rule of Pericles?

_____

_____

_____

_____

What happened when Sparta and Athens went to war for control of Greece?

_____

_____

_____

_____

Read To Write Challenge

Pericles stated, "We do not say that a man who takes no interest in politics minds his own business. We say he has no business here at all." On a separate sheet of paper, use Pericles's quote as the introduction to a **persuasive paragraph** *convincing people to vote.*

Copyright © by The McGraw-Hill Companies, Inc.

Chapter 7, Section 4

Chapter 8, Section 1
The Culture of Ancient Greece

(Pages 376–385)

Main Idea

Setting a Purpose for Reading Think about these questions as you read:
• What were the main religious beliefs of the Greeks?
• How did Greek art and architecture reflect Greek ideas?

Reading Strategy

As you read pages 377–385 in your textbook, complete this Venn diagram showing the similarities and differences between an epic and a fable.

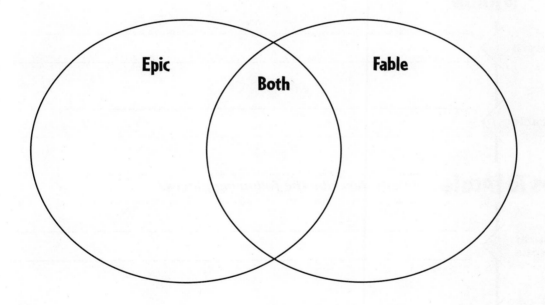

Epic   Both   Fable

Copyright © by The McGraw-Hill Companies, Inc.

 Notes

Greek Mythology *(pages 377–378)*

Previewing

Have you ever read a Greek myth? Preview this section to get an idea of what is ahead. First, skim the section. Then write a sentence or two explaining what you think you will be learning. After you have finished reading, revise your statements as necessary.

_____

_____

_____

_____

_____

Terms To Know

Define or describe the following terms from this lesson.

myth _____

_____

oracle _____

_____

Places To Locate

Briefly describe the following places.

Mount Olympus _____

_____

Delphi _____

_____

Copyright © by The McGraw-Hill Companies, Inc.

Academic Vocabulary

Define this academic vocabulary word from this lesson.

grant

_____

_____

Sum It Up

Why did the Greeks have rituals and festivals for their gods and goddesses?

_____

_____

_____

Greek Poetry and Fables *(pages 379–380)*

Summarizing

As you read, write one sentence summarizing each of the following stories and fables.

The *Odyssey*

_____

_____

The *Iliad*

_____

_____

"The Tortoise and the Hare"

_____

_____

Terms To Know

Define or describe the following terms from this lesson.

epic

_____

_____

fable

_____

_____

Copyright © by The McGraw-Hill Companies, Inc.

Chapter 8, Section 1

People To Meet

Explain why each of these people is important.

Homer _____

_____

_____

Aesop _____

_____

Academic Vocabulary

Define these academic vocabulary words from this lesson.

generation _____

_____

_____

tradition _____

_____

Sum It Up

What are the characteristics of a fable?

_____

_____

_____

_____

_____

Copyright © by The McGraw-Hill Companies, Inc.

Greek Drama *(pages 382–383)*

Connecting

What are your favorite television shows and movies? As you read, compare the dramas, comedies, and tragedies you watch with Greek drama. Summarize your thoughts in a paragraph. Be sure to address the similarities and differences that you see.

_____

_____

_____

_____

Terms To Know

Define or describe the following terms from this lesson.

drama

_____

_____

tragedy

_____

_____

comedy

_____

_____

People To Meet

Explain why each of these people is important.

Sophocles

_____

_____

Euripides

_____

_____

Copyright © by The McGraw-Hill Companies, Inc.

Key Points

Academic Vocabulary

Define the following academic vocabulary word from this lesson.

conflict _____

_____

Sum It Up

What two types of drama did the Greeks create?

_____

_____

_____

_____

Greek Art and Architecture (pages 384–385)

Synthesizing

As you read, find information to answer the first two questions. Then use these answers to respond to the third question below.

1. What beliefs and ideas are reflected in Greek art and architecture?

_____

_____

2. Where do we see examples of Greek architecture today?

_____

_____

3. Synthesize: How has ancient Greece influenced our culture today?

_____

_____

Copyright © by The McGraw-Hill Companies, Inc.

 **Key Points**

 **Notes**

Copyright © by The McGraw-Hill Companies, Inc.

Sum It Up

What was the most important type of building in ancient Greece?

_____

_____

_____

Section Wrap-up

Now that you have read the section, write the answers to the questions that were included in **Setting a Purpose for Reading** *at the beginning of the lesson.*

What were the main religious beliefs of the Greeks?

_____

_____

_____

_____

_____

_____

How did Greek art and architecture reflect Greek ideas?

_____

_____

_____

_____

_____

Read To Write Challenge

Use library resources or the Internet to research the Greek god Dionysus. On a separate sheet of paper, write an expository essay explaining how the worship of Dionysus led to the emergence of theater.

Chapter 8, Section 2
Greek Philosophy and History

(Pages 392–397)

Main Idea

Setting a Purpose for Reading Think about these questions as you read:
- What ideas did Greek philosophers develop?
- How did Greeks contribute to the history of Western civilization?

Reading Strategy

As you read pages 393–397 in your textbook, complete a diagram like this one to show the basic philosophies of Socrates.

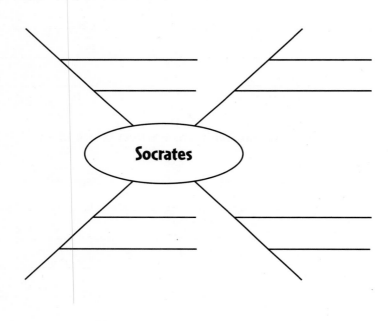

Copyright © by The McGraw-Hill Companies, Inc.

Greek Philosophers *(pages 393–395)*

Reviewing

Complete the following reading guide by filling in the important ideas from each of these Greek philosophers. Use your guide to review main points from your reading.

Philosopher	Ideas
Pythagoras	
Socrates	
Plato	
Aristotle	

Terms To Know

Define or describe the following terms from this lesson.

philosophy

philosopher

Sophist

Socratic method

Copyright © by The McGraw-Hill Companies, Inc.

Academic Vocabulary

Define this academic vocabulary word from this lesson.

> **reject**

_____

_____

Terms To Review

Use each of these terms that you studied earlier in a sentence that reflects the term's meaning.

> **tyrant**
> (Chapter 7, Section 2)

_____

_____

> **oligarchy**
> (Chapter 7, Section 2)

_____

_____

Sum It Up

How did Aristotle's idea of government differ from Plato's?

_____

_____

_____

_____

Copyright © by The McGraw-Hill Companies, Inc.

Greek Historians (page 397)

Skimming

Quickly look over the entire selection to get a general idea about the reading. Then briefly describe what the selection is about on the lines below.

_____

_____

_____

_____

People To Meet

Explain why each of these people is important.

Herodotus

_____

_____

Thucydides

_____

_____

Academic Vocabulary

Define this academic vocabulary word from this lesson.

accurate

_____

_____

Copyright © by The McGraw-Hill Companies, Inc.

Sum It Up

How did Thucydides view war and politics?

_____

_____

_____

_____

Section Wrap-up

Now that you have read the section, write the answers to the questions that were included in **Setting a Purpose for Reading** *at the beginning of the lesson.*

What ideas did Greek philosophers develop?

_____

_____

_____

_____

_____

How did Greeks contribute to the history of Western civilization?

_____

_____

_____

_____

Read To Write Challenge

Research the Socratic method. On a separate sheet of paper, write a narrative essay *that includes dialogue of one person applying the method to a second person's statement.*

Copyright © by The McGraw-Hill Companies, Inc.

Chapter 8, Section 3
Alexander the Great
(Pages 398–403)

Main Idea

Setting a Purpose for Reading Think about these questions as you read:
- How did Philip II of Macedonia unite the Greek states?
- How did Alexander the Great change history?

Reading Strategy

As you read pages 399–403 in your textbook, complete this diagram to track the achievements of Alexander the Great.

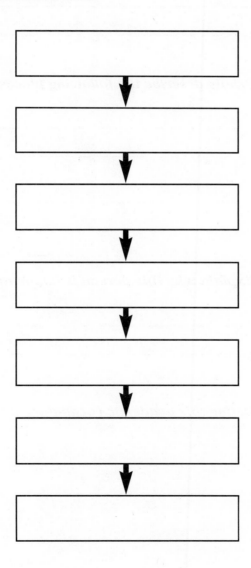

Copyright © by The McGraw-Hill Companies, Inc.

Macedonia Attacks Greece *(pages 399–400)*

Predicting

Think about all you have learned about Greece up to this point. Now, before you read, answer the question below. What do you predict will happen? After you read, write a brief paragraph about your reaction to the actual events.

Will Macedonia defeat the Greeks?

_____

_____

_____

_____

_____

Places To Locate

Briefly describe the following places.

Macedonia

_____

_____

_____

Chaeronea

_____

_____

People To Meet

Explain why this person is important.

Philip II

_____

_____

Academic Vocabulary

Define this academic vocabulary word from this lesson.

achieve

_____

_____

Copyright © by The McGraw-Hill Companies, Inc.

Sum It Up + **Why did Philip II invade Greece?**

_____

_____

_____

_____

Alexander Builds an Empire (pages 400–403)

Previewing *Look at the headings and write a question about each one. Find answers to your questions as you read. Revise your question if the answer is not found in the reading.*

I. Alexander Builds an Empire

_____

II. What Did Alexander Conquer?

_____

III. Alexander's Legacy

_____

IV. The Empire Breaks Apart

_____

Terms To Know *Define or describe the following terms from this lesson.*

legacy >

_____

_____

Hellenistic Era >

_____

_____

Copyright © by The McGraw-Hill Companies, Inc.

Chapter 8, Section 3

Places To Locate

Briefly describe the following places.

Syria >
_____
_____
_____

Alexandria >
_____
_____

Academic Vocabulary

Define this academic vocabulary word from this lesson.

military >
_____
_____

Terms To Review

Use this term that you studied earlier in a sentence that reflects the term's meaning.

satrap
(Chapter 7, Section 3) >
_____
_____

Sum It Up

What was Alexander's legacy?

_____
_____
_____
_____

Copyright © by The McGraw-Hill Companies, Inc.

*Now that you have read the section, write the answers to the questions that were included in **Setting a Purpose for Reading** at the beginning of the lesson.*

How did Philip II of Macedonia unite the Greek states?

_____

_____

_____

_____

_____

_____

How did Alexander the Great change history?

_____

_____

_____

_____

_____

_____

Read To Write Challenge

*Research Alexander the Great's military tactics. On a separate sheet of paper, write a **persuasive essay** that explains how you see Alexander. Use facts to support your position.*

Copyright © by The McGraw-Hill Companies, Inc.

Chapter 8, Section 4
The Spread of Greek Culture

(Pages 406-411)

Main Idea

Setting a Purpose for Reading Think about these questions as you read:
- How did Greek culture spread and develop in the Hellenistic Era?
- Who were Epicurus and Zeno?

Reading Strategy

As you read pages 407-411 in your textbook, create a diagram to show the major Greek contributions to Western civilization.

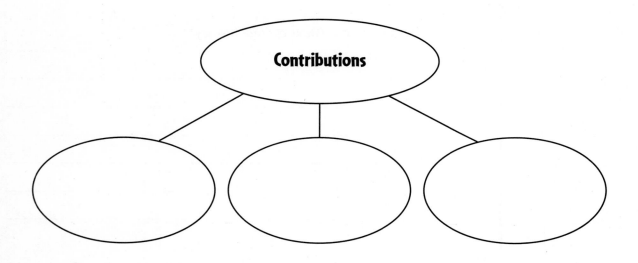

Copyright © by The McGraw-Hill Companies, Inc.

Greek Culture Spreads (page 407)

Determining the Main Idea

As you read, list the causes and effects of the spread of Greek culture in the Hellenistic Era.

Greek Culture Spreads	
Causes	**Effects**

Sum It Up

How did the Hellenistic kingdoms spread Greek culture?

_____

_____

_____

_____

New Philosophy and Science (pages 408–410)

Responding

What is true happiness, and what really makes people happy in life? Consider the views of the Epicureans and the Stoics. Then write a paragraph responding to their views and stating your own views about personal happiness.

_____

_____

_____

_____

Copyright © by The McGraw-Hill Companies, Inc.

Terms To Know

Define or describe the following terms from this lesson.

Epicureanism
_____
_____

Stoicism
_____
_____

astronomer
_____
_____

plane geometry
_____
_____

solid geometry
_____
_____

Academic Vocabulary

Define these three academic vocabulary words.

goal
_____
_____

lecture
_____
_____

major
_____
_____

Copyright © by The McGraw-Hill Companies, Inc.

Terms To Review

Use each of these terms that you studied earlier in a sentence that reflects the term's meaning.

philosopher
(Chapter 8, Section 2)

_____

_____

_____

philosophy
(Chapter 8, Section 2)

_____

_____

Sum It Up

Who was the most famous scientist of the Hellenistic Era? What did he contribute?

_____

_____

_____

Copyright © by The McGraw-Hill Companies, Inc.

 **Key Points**

 **Notes**

Copyright © by The McGraw-Hill Companies, Inc.

Section Wrap-up

Now that you have read the section, write the answers to the questions that were included in **Setting a Purpose for Reading** *at the beginning of the lesson.*

How did Greek culture spread and develop in the Hellenistic Era?

_____

_____

_____

_____

_____

Who were Epicurus and Zeno?

_____

_____

_____

_____

_____

Read To Write Challenge

Research the poetry of Theocritus. On a separate sheet of paper, write a **descriptive poem** *about Greece's legacy to the world using Theocritus's form.*

Chapter 9, Section 1
Rome's Beginnings

(Pages 420–425)

Main Idea

Setting a Purpose for Reading Think about these questions as you read:
- How did geography play a role in the rise of Roman civilization?
- How did the Romans build Rome from a small city into a great power?

Reading Strategy

As you read pages 421–425 in your textbook, complete this diagram to show how the Etruscans affected the development of Rome.

Etruscans

Copyright © by The McGraw-Hill Companies, Inc.

The Origins of Rome (pages 421–423)

Summarizing

Two different legends describe how Rome began. As you read, take notes on these two legends. Then write a two or three sentence summary of each legend.

Romulus and Remus >

_____

_____

_____

_____

_____

The _Aeneid_ >

_____

_____

_____

People To Meet

Explain why these people are important.

Latins >

_____

_____

Etruscans >

_____

_____

Places To Locate

Briefly describe the following places.

Sicily >

_____

_____

Apennines >

_____

_____

Latium >

_____

Copyright © by The McGraw-Hill Companies, Inc.

 **Key Points**  **Notes**

Tiber River

_____

_____

_____

Etruria

_____

_____

_____

Academic Vocabulary

Define these academic vocabulary words from this lesson.

isolate

_____

_____

_____

capacity

_____

_____

_____

Terms To Review

Use each of these terms that you studied earlier in a sentence that reflects the term's meaning.

peninsula
(Chapter 7, Section 1)

_____

_____

epic
(Chapter 8, Section 1)

_____

_____

Sum It Up

How did geography help the Romans prosper?

_____

_____

_____

_____

Copyright © by The McGraw-Hill Companies, Inc.

The Birth of a Republic *(pages 423–425)*

Reviewing

What made Rome so strong? As you read, complete the diagram below. Use this diagram to review your learning.

Rome's Strength

Terms To Know

Define or describe the following terms from this lesson.

republic > _____
_____
_____

legion > _____
_____
_____

People To Meet

Explain why this group is important.

Tarquins > _____
_____
_____

Academic Vocabulary

Define these academic vocabulary words from this lesson.

chapter > _____
_____
_____

status > _____
_____
_____

Copyright © by The McGraw-Hill Companies, Inc.

Sum It Up *How did Rome rule its new conquests?*

_____

_____

_____

_____

Section Wrap-up *Now that you have read the section, write the answers to the questions that were included in Setting a Purpose for Reading at the beginning of the lesson.*

How did geography play a role in the rise of Roman civilization?

_____

_____

_____

_____

How did the Romans build Rome from a small city into a great power?

_____

_____

_____

_____

Read To Write Challenge *Research the burial practices of the Etruscans. On a separate sheet of paper, write an expository essay explaining the Etruscan banquet, catacombs, "tombs of gold," and the necropolis outside of each Etruscan city.*

Copyright © by The McGraw-Hill Companies, Inc.

Chapter 9, Section 2
The Roman Republic

(Pages 426–434)

Main Idea

Setting a Purpose for Reading Think about these questions as you read:
- How did Rome's government change?
- How did Rome gain control of the Mediterranean region?

Reading Strategy

As you read pages 427–434 in your textbook, complete this chart listing the government officials and legislative bodies of the Roman Republic.

Officials	Legislative Bodies

Copyright © by The McGraw-Hill Companies, Inc.

Rome's Government *(pages 427–429)*

Questioning — *Before you read, scan the subsection. Write a question for each part of the lesson. Then after you read, write the answers to your questions.*

I. Rome's Government

_____

_____

II. How Did Rome's Government Work?

_____

_____

III. Plebeians Against Patricians

_____

_____

IV. Who Was Cincinnatus?

_____

_____

Copyright © by The McGraw-Hill Companies, Inc.

 **Key Points**

 **Notes**

Terms To Know

Define or describe the following terms from this lesson.

patrician ⟩ _____
_____

plebeian ⟩ _____
_____

consul ⟩ _____
_____

veto ⟩ _____
_____

praetor ⟩ _____
_____

dictator ⟩ _____
_____

Academic Vocabulary

Define these academic vocabulary words from this lesson.

legislate ⟩ _____
_____

accommodate ⟩ _____
_____

Copyright © by The McGraw-Hill Companies, Inc.

Sum It Up

What checks and balances existed in the Roman Republic's government?

_____

_____

_____

_____

Roman Law (page 431)

Connecting

How did the Roman system of law affect the legal system we enjoy today? As you read, describe the standards of justice developed for the Twelve Tables and the Law of Nations. Then write a brief paragraph about the impact these principles have on you today.

Twelve Tables:

_____

_____

Law of Nations:

_____

_____

How These Principles Affect Me Today:

_____

_____

_____

Copyright © by The McGraw-Hill Companies, Inc.

Key Points

Notes

Terms To Review

Use each of these terms that you studied earlier in a sentence that reflects the term's meaning.

patrician
(Chapter 9, Section 2)

_____

_____

_____

plebian
(Chapter 9, Section 2)

_____

_____

Sum It Up

What is the "rule of law," and why is it important?

_____

_____

_____

_____

Copyright © by The McGraw-Hill Companies, Inc.

Rome Expands (pages 432–434)

Sequencing
As you read, number the following events in the correct order.

1. ____ Hannibal attacks Rome.

2. ____ Romans lose the Battle of Cannae.

3. ____ Scipio's troops defeat the Carthaginians.

4. ____ First Punic War begins.

5. ____ Rome crushes Carthage's navy off the coast of Sicily.

6. ____ Carthage expands its empire into southern Spain.

7. ____ Rome gains its first province in Asia.

8. ____ Scipio invades Carthage.

9. ____ Macedonia comes under Roman rule.

Places To Locate
Briefly describe the following places.

Carthage _____

_____

Cannae _____

_____

Zama _____

_____

Copyright © by The McGraw-Hill Companies, Inc.

Chapter 9, Section 2

159

Notes

People To Meet

Explain why these people are important.

Hannibal

_____

_____

Scipio

_____

_____

Academic Vocabulary

Define this academic vocabulary word from this lesson.

challenge

_____

_____

Sum It Up

How did Rome punish Carthage at the end of the Third Punic War?

_____

_____

_____

_____

Copyright © by The McGraw-Hill Companies, Inc.

Copyright © by The McGraw-Hill Companies, Inc.

Now that you have read the section, write the answers to the questions that were included in **Setting a Purpose for Reading** *at the beginning of the lesson.*

How did Rome's government change?

_____

_____

_____

_____

_____

_____

How did Rome gain control of the Mediterranean region?

_____

_____

_____

_____

_____

_____

Read To Write Challenge

Research King Pyrrhus of Epirus. On a separate sheet of paper, write a descriptive paragraph *about him and the meaning of the term "Pyrrhic victory."*

Chapter 9, Section 2

161

Chapter 9, Section 3
The Fall of the Republic

(Pages 435–441)

Main Idea

Setting a Purpose for Reading Think about these questions as you read:
- What impact did Julius Caesar have on Rome?
- Why did the Roman Republic become an empire under Augustus?

Reading Strategy

As you read pages 436–441 in your textbook, complete this chart to identify the main ideas of Section 3 and supporting details.

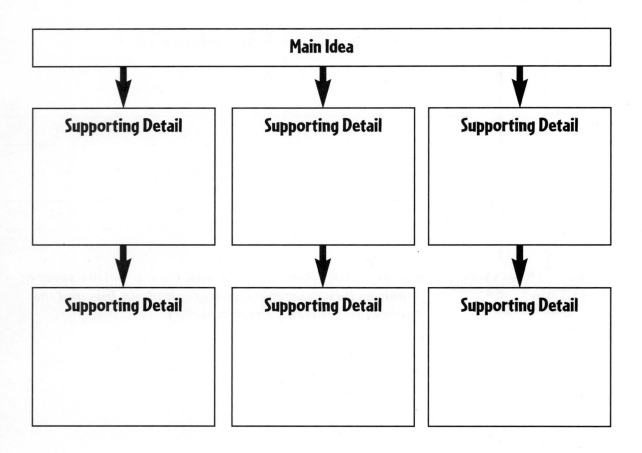

Main Idea

Supporting Detail	Supporting Detail	Supporting Detail

Supporting Detail	Supporting Detail	Supporting Detail

Copyright © by The McGraw-Hill Companies, Inc.

Trouble in the Republic *(pages 436–437)*

Monitoring Comprehension

What factors worked together to weaken the republic? Complete the diagram below to identify the main factors.

```
┌──────────────┐ _____
│ Trouble in the │ _____
│  Republic    │ _____
└──────────────┘ _____
                 _____
```

Terms To Know

Define or describe the following term from this lesson.

latifundia _____
_____

Academic Vocabulary

Define these academic vocabulary words from this lesson.

despite _____
_____

estate _____
_____

Sum It Up

What change did Marius make to the Roman army?

_____
_____
_____
_____

Copyright © by The McGraw-Hill Companies, Inc.

Julius Caesar *(pages 438–439)*

Drawing Conclusions

As you read, list the accomplishments, actions, and reforms of Julius Caesar. Then, after you have read the passage, write a general statement about Caesar. Your list of accomplishments and reforms should support your statement.

Accomplishments, Actions, and Reforms:

_____

_____

_____

_____

_____

_____

Conclusion

_____

_____

Terms To Know

Define or describe the following term from this lesson.

triumvirate

_____

_____

Places To Locate

Briefly describe the following place.

Rubicon

_____

_____

Copyright © by The McGraw-Hill Companies, Inc.

Sum It Up *Why did Brutus, Cassius, and others kill Caesar?*

_____

_____

_____

_____

Rome Becomes an Empire *(pages 440–441)*

Connecting *How did the ideas of Cicero affect the writers of the U.S. Constitution? How do these ideas affect your life today? As you read, list the ideas that influenced the founders of our country. Then write a brief paragraph about the impact these values have on you today.*

Cicero's Ideas:

_____

_____

_____

How These Ideas Affect Me Today:

_____

_____

_____

Places To Locate *Briefly describe the following place.*

Actium ⟩ _____

_____

Copyright © by The McGraw-Hill Companies, Inc.

 Notes

People To Meet

Explain why each of these people is important.

Octavian
_____
_____

Antony
_____
_____

Cicero
_____
_____

Augustus
_____
_____

Academic Vocabulary

Define these academic vocabulary words from this lesson.

sole
_____
_____

foundation
_____
_____

Sum It Up

How did the Battle of Actium affect the history of Rome?

_____
_____
_____
_____

Copyright © by The McGraw-Hill Companies, Inc.

Now that you have read the section, write the answers to the questions that were included in **Setting a Purpose for Reading** *at the beginning of the lesson.*

What impact did Julius Caesar have on Rome?

_____

_____

_____

_____

_____

_____

Why did the Roman Republic become an empire under Augustus?

_____

_____

_____

_____

_____

_____

Read To Write Challenge

Research Julius Caesar's rise to power. On a separate sheet of paper, write a **persuasive paragraph** *either for or against Caesar as ruler.*

Copyright © by The McGraw-Hill Companies, Inc.

Chapter 9, Section 4
The Early Empire

(Pages 444–451)

Main Idea

Setting a Purpose for Reading Think about these questions as you read:
• How did Augustus create a new era of prosperity?
• What changes made the empire rich and prosperous?

Reading Strategy

As you read pages 445–451 in your textbook, complete this chart to show the changes Augustus made in the Roman Empire and the effect of each change.

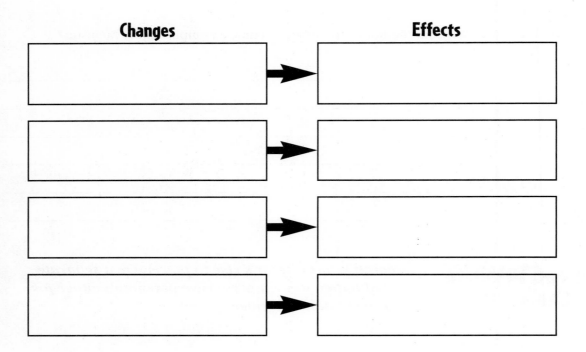

Changes   **Effects**

Copyright © by The McGraw-Hill Companies, Inc.

The Emperor Augustus (pages 445–446)

Drawing Conclusions

Augustus paved the way for 200 years of peace and prosperity. Why do you think the Roman Empire remained at peace even with weak emperors such as Caligula and Nero?

_____

_____

_____

_____

_____

_____

Terms To Know

Define or describe the following term from this lesson.

Pax Romana >

_____

_____

People To Meet

Explain why these people are important.

Caligula >

_____

_____

Nero >

_____

_____

Academic Vocabulary

Define these academic vocabulary words from this lesson.

successor >

_____

_____

commit >

_____

_____

Copyright © by The McGraw-Hill Companies, Inc.

Copyright © by The McGraw-Hill Companies, Inc.

Sum It Up *What did Augustus do to make the empire safer and stronger?*

_____

_____

_____

Unity and Prosperity *(pages 446–451)*

Outlining *Complete this outline as you read.*

I. Unity and Prosperity

    A. _____

    B. _____

II. The "Good Emperors"

    A. _____

    B. _____

III. A Unified Empire

    A. _____

    B. _____

IV. A Booming Economy

    A. _____

    B. _____

V. Roads and Money

    A. _____

    B. _____

VI. Ongoing Inequality

    A. _____

Terms To Know

Define or describe the following terms from this lesson.

aqueduct

_____

_____

_____

currency

_____

_____

_____

Places To Locate

Briefly describe the following places.

Rhine River

_____

_____

_____

Danube River

_____

_____

_____

Puteoli

_____

_____

_____

Ostia

_____

_____

Academic Vocabulary

Define this academic vocabulary word from this lesson.

capable

_____

_____

Copyright © by The McGraw-Hill Companies, Inc.

Key Points

Notes

Sum It Up

Who were the "good emperors," and what did they accomplish?

_____

_____

_____

_____

Section Wrap-up

*Now that you have read the section, write the answers to the questions that were included in **Setting a Purpose for Reading** at the beginning of the lesson.*

How did Augustus create a new era of prosperity?

_____

_____

_____

_____

What changes made the empire rich and prosperous?

_____

_____

_____

_____

Read To Write Challenge

Research one of the good (or bad) emperors discussed in this section. On a separate sheet of paper, write a biographical sketch of the emperor.

Copyright © by The McGraw-Hill Companies, Inc.

Chapter 10, Section 1
Life in Ancient Rome

(Pages 460–468)

Main Idea

Setting a Purpose for Reading Think about these questions as you read:
- How did Roman culture develop and change?
- What was life like in the Roman Empire?

Reading Strategy

As you read pages 461–468 in your textbook, complete this Venn diagram to show similarities and differences between the rich and the poor in Rome.

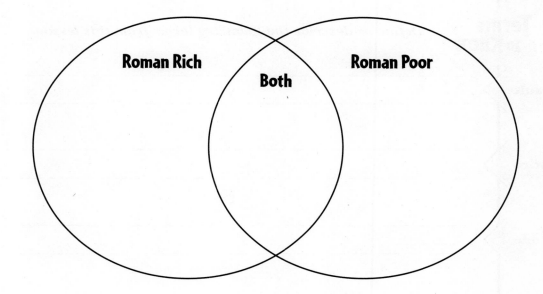

Roman Rich   **Both**   **Roman Poor**

Copyright © by The McGraw-Hill Companies, Inc.

Roman Culture (pages 461–463)

Synthesizing

Roman historians took different views of the Roman Empire. After you read the entire passage, read the views of Livy and Tacitus again (page 462). Now you play the historian. Using all you have read and learned about Rome up to this point, write your own view of the empire.

_____

_____

_____

_____

_____

Terms To Know

Define or describe the following terms from this lesson.

vault

_____

_____

satire

_____

_____

ode

_____

_____

anatomy

_____

People To Meet

Explain why these people are important.

Virgil

_____

_____

Horace

_____

_____

Copyright © by The McGraw-Hill Companies, Inc.

 Key Points

 Notes

> Galen
_____
_____
_____

> Ptolemy
_____
_____

Academic Vocabulary

Define this academic vocabulary word from this lesson.

> technique
_____
_____

Terms To Review

Use this term that you studied earlier in a sentence that reflects the term's meaning.

> myth
(Chapter 8, Section 1)
_____
_____

Sum It Up

How did Romans improve on Greek ideas in architecture?

_____
_____
_____
_____

Copyright © by The McGraw-Hill Companies, Inc.

Daily Life in Rome (pages 464–468)

Inferring

The Roman government provided "bread and circuses," or free grain and entertainment. Based on your reading, why do you think the government thought this was necessary? Write a brief paragraph to answer this question. Support your answer with facts from your reading.

_____

_____

_____

_____

_____

Terms To Know

Define or describe the following terms from this lesson.

Forum

_____

_____

gladiator

_____

_____

paterfamilias

_____

_____

rhetoric

_____

_____

People To Meet

Explain why this person is important.

Spartacus

_____

_____

Copyright © by The McGraw-Hill Companies, Inc.

Academic Vocabulary

Define this academic vocabulary word from this lesson.

constant

_____

_____

Sum It Up

Compare the life of upper-class women to women of other classes.

_____

_____

_____

Section Wrap-up

Now that you have read the section, write the answers to the questions that were included in **Setting a Purpose for Reading** *at the beginning of the lesson.*

How did Roman culture develop and change?

_____

_____

_____

_____

What was life like in the Roman Empire?

_____

_____

_____

_____

Read To Write Challenge

Research the eruption of Mount Vesuvius in A.D. 79. On a separate sheet of paper, write a **descriptive essay** *about what happened to Pompeii, and what types of artifacts archaeologists uncovered there.*

Copyright © by The McGraw-Hill Companies, Inc.

Chapter 10, Section 2
The Fall of Rome

(Pages 474–483)

Main Idea

Setting a Purpose for Reading Think about these questions as you read:
- Why was the Roman Empire weakened?
- How would our world be different today if the Roman Empire had never existed?

Reading Strategy

As you read pages 475–483 in your textbook, complete the diagram to show the events that led up to the fall of the Roman Empire.

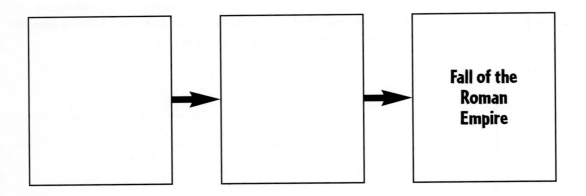

```
┌──────────┐      ┌──────────┐      ┌──────────┐
│          │      │          │      │ Fall of the │
│          │ ───▶ │          │ ───▶ │  Roman    │
│          │      │          │      │  Empire   │
└──────────┘      └──────────┘      └──────────┘
```

Copyright © by The McGraw-Hill Companies, Inc.

The Decline of Rome *(pages 475–477)*

Summarizing

Use the chart below to summarize the reforms made by Diocletian and Constantine.

Diocletian's Reforms	Constantine's Reforms

Terms To Know

Define or describe the following terms from this lesson.

inflation _____

_____

barter _____

_____

reform _____

_____

Copyright © by The McGraw-Hill Companies, Inc.

Places To Locate

Briefly describe the following place.

Constantinople

_____

_____

Academic Vocabulary

Define this academic vocabulary word from this lesson.

authority

_____

_____

Sum It Up

How did Diocletian try to reverse the decline of Rome?

_____

_____

_____

Rome Falls _(pages 479–481)_

Scanning

Glance quickly over the reading to find answers to the following questions.

1. What happened to the empire in A.D. 395?

_____

_____

2. Why did Germanic groups invade the empire?

_____

_____

Copyright © by The McGraw-Hill Companies, Inc.

Notes

3. What happened at the Battle of Adrianople?

_____

_____

4. Who was Alaric?

_____

_____

5. Who was Odoacer?

_____

_____

People To Meet

Explain why this person is important.

Theodosius >

_____

_____

Sum It Up

Which event usually marks the fall of the Western Roman Empire?

_____

_____

_____

_____

Copyright © by The McGraw-Hill Companies, Inc.

The Legacy of Rome *(pages 482–483)*

Reviewing

Use the chart below to take notes on the legacies of Rome. Use your completed chart to review key concepts from your reading.

The Legacy of Rome		
Government	**Culture**	**Religion**

Academic Vocabulary

Define this academic vocabulary word from this lesson.

expand ⟩ _____

_____

Terms To Review

Use this term that you studied earlier in a sentence that reflects the term's meaning.

republic
(Chapter 9, Section 1) ⟩ _____

_____

Copyright © by The McGraw-Hill Companies, Inc.

 Key Points

 Notes

Sum It Up

Which aspects of Rome are reflected in present-day cultures?

_____

_____

_____

_____

Section Wrap-up

Now that you have read the section, write the answers to the questions that were included in **Setting a Purpose for Reading** *at the beginning of the lesson.*

Why was the Roman Empire weakened?

_____

_____

_____

_____

How would our world be different today if the Roman Empire had never existed?

_____

_____

_____

_____

Read To Write Challenge

Research the Latin origin of many English words. Scan a dictionary to find at least 20 Latin-based words. On a separate sheet of paper, write your list as well as an expository paragraph explaining the Latin categorization of species.

Copyright © by The McGraw-Hill Companies, Inc.

Chapter 10, Section 3
The Byzantine Empire

(Pages 484–491)

Main Idea

Setting a Purpose for Reading Think about these questions as you read:
- What policies and reforms made the Byzantine Empire strong?
- What ideas and beliefs shaped Byzantine culture?

Reading Strategy

As you read pages 485–491 in your textbook, complete this chart to show the causes and effects of Justinian's new law code.

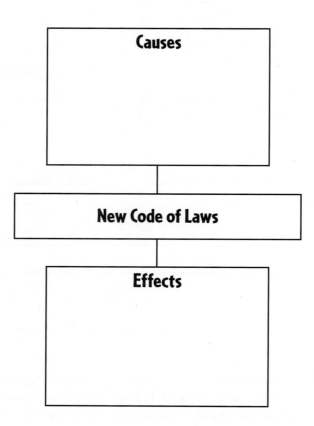

Causes

New Code of Laws

Effects

Copyright © by The McGraw-Hill Companies, Inc.

The Rise of the Byzantines *(pages 485–486)*

Previewing

Preview this section to get an idea of what is ahead. First, skim the section. Then write a sentence or two explaining what you think you will be learning. After you have finished reading, revise your statements as necessary.

_____

_____

_____

_____

_____

_____

Places To Locate

Briefly describe the following places.

Black Sea

_____

_____

Aegean Sea

_____

_____

Copyright © by The McGraw-Hill Companies, Inc.

Terms To Review

Use this term that you studied earlier in a sentence that reflects the term's meaning.

peninsula
(Chapter 7, Section 1)

_____

_____

Sum It Up

Why did the Byzantine Empire have such a blending of cultures?

_____

_____

_____

_____

Emperor Justinian (pages 486–487)

Determining the Main Idea

As you read, write the main idea of the passage. Review your statement when you have finished reading and revise as needed.

_____

_____

_____

_____

_____

Copyright © by The McGraw-Hill Companies, Inc.

People To Meet

Explain why these people are important.

Justinian >

_____

_____

Theodora >

_____

_____

Belisarius >

_____

_____

Tribonian >

_____

_____

Academic Vocabulary

Define these academic vocabulary words from this lesson.

income >

_____

_____

rely >

_____

_____

Sum It Up

What did Justinian accomplish during his reign?

_____

_____

_____

_____

Copyright © by The McGraw-Hill Companies, Inc.

Byzantine Civilization (pages 489–491)

Outlining   *Complete this outline as you read.*

I. The Importance of Trade

    A. _____

    B. _____

II. Byzantine Art and Architecture

    A. _____

    B. _____

III. Byzantine Women

    A. _____

    B. _____

IV. Byzantine Education

    A. _____

    B. _____

Terms To Know   *Define or describe the following terms from this lesson.*

mosaic _____
_____

saint _____
_____

regent _____
_____

Copyright © by The McGraw-Hill Companies, Inc.

 **Key Points**

 **Notes**

Academic Vocabulary

Define this academic vocabulary word from this lesson.

enormous

_____

_____

Terms To Review

Use this term that you studied earlier in a sentence that reflects the term's meaning.

caravan
(Chapter 1, Section 3)

_____

_____

Sum It Up

What church is one of Justinian's greatest achievements?

_____

_____

_____

_____

_____

Copyright © by The McGraw-Hill Companies, Inc.

 **Key Points**

 **Notes**

Section Wrap-up

Now that you have read the section, write the answers to the questions that were included in **Setting a Purpose for Reading** *at the beginning of the lesson.*

What policies and reforms made the Byzantine Empire strong?

_____

_____

_____

_____

_____

_____

What ideas and beliefs shaped Byzantine culture?

_____

_____

_____

_____

_____

_____

Read To Write Challenge

Research the Justinian Code. On a separate sheet of paper, write an expository paragraph *explaining the four parts to the Code.*

Copyright © by The McGraw-Hill Companies, Inc.

Chapter 11, Section 1
The First Christians

(Pages 500–508)

Main Idea

Setting a Purpose for Reading Think about these questions as you read:
- What did Jesus teach?
- How did people react to his teachings?

Reading Strategy

As you read pages 501–508 in your textbook, complete this diagram to show the purposes of the early Christian churches.

Purposes of Churches

The Jews and the Romans (page 501)

Connecting

The Jews responded in different ways to Roman rule. Some worked with the Romans. Some followed their own traditions more closely. Some moved away. Others rebelled. How do you feel when someone else—maybe a parent, teacher, peer, or other leader—is in control of your life? How do you respond when this person shares your values and beliefs? How do you respond when they do not? Write a brief paragraph answering these questions.

_____

_____

_____

_____

_____

Places To Locate

Briefly describe the following places.

Jerusalem

_____

_____

Judaea

_____

_____

Sum It Up

Why did the Jews leave Judaea after the A.D. 132 revolt?

_____

_____

_____

_____

Copyright © by The McGraw-Hill Companies, Inc.

The Life of Jesus (pages 502–505)

Responding

This section states that Jesus taught in parables. The parable of the Good Samaritan is one of the best known parables. As you read that parable, consider your personal response to it. Also consider why Jesus presented his teachings in the form of parables. Write your response in a brief paragraph.

_____

_____

_____

_____

_____

_____

_____

Terms To Know

Define or describe the following terms from this lesson.

messiah >

_____

_____

disciple >

_____

_____

parable >

_____

_____

resurrection >

_____

_____

Copyright © by The McGraw-Hill Companies, Inc.

 Key Points

 Notes

Places To Locate

Briefly describe the following places.

Jerusalem

_____
_____

Nazareth

_____
_____

Galilee

_____
_____

Academic Vocabulary

Define this academic vocabulary word from this lesson.

decade

_____
_____

Sum It Up

What were the main ideas Jesus taught during his life?

_____
_____
_____
_____

Copyright © by The McGraw-Hill Companies, Inc.

The First Christians *(pages 506–508)*

Predicting

On the chart below, write headings that indicate the kind of information you expect to find in the reading. Use the Main Idea, Reading Connection, main headings, and terms to help you with the headings. The first one has been done for you. Then as you read, write details from the text under the correct headings.

Early Christians		

Copyright © by The McGraw-Hill Companies, Inc.

Terms To Know

Define or describe the following terms from this lesson.

apostle

_____

_____

salvation

_____

_____

Academic Vocabulary

Define this academic vocabulary word from this lesson.

reside

_____

_____

Sum It Up

Who were Peter and Paul, and why were they important?

_____

_____

_____

_____

Copyright © by The McGraw-Hill Companies, Inc.

Now that you have read the section, write the answers to the questions that were included in **Setting a Purpose for Reading** *at the beginning of the lesson.*

What did Jesus teach?

_____

_____

_____

_____

_____

_____

How did people react to his teachings?

_____

_____

_____

_____

_____

_____

Read To Write Challenge

Reread the parable of the Good Samaritan. Then, on a separate sheet of paper, rewrite the parable in a narrative form. However, your parable should be written as if the story took place in modern times.

Copyright © by The McGraw-Hill Companies, Inc.

Chapter 11, Section 2
The Christian Church

(Pages 509–514)

Main Idea

Setting a Purpose for Reading Think about these questions as you read:
- How did Christianity become the official religion of the Roman Empire?
- How was the early Christian Church organized?

Reading Strategy

As you read pages 510–514 in your textbook, complete the diagram to show reasons for the growth of Christianity.

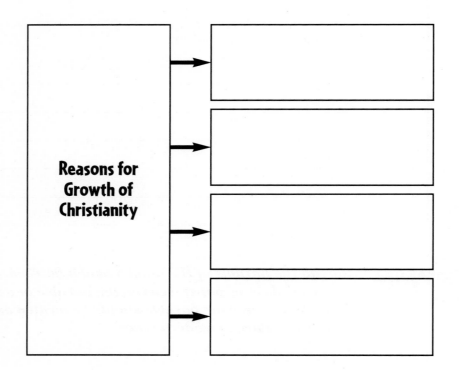

Reasons for Growth of Christianity

Copyright © by The McGraw-Hill Companies, Inc.

A Growing Faith (pages 510–512)

Inferring   *As you read, infer the answer to the following question.*

Why did Christians refuse to serve in the army or hold public office?

_____

_____

_____

Terms To Know   *Define or describe the following terms from this lesson.*

persecute

_____

_____

martyr

_____

People To Meet   *Explain why these people are important.*

Constantine

_____

_____

Helena

_____

_____

Theodosius

_____

_____

Copyright © by The McGraw-Hill Companies, Inc.

Key Points

Notes

Academic Vocabulary

Define these academic vocabulary words from this lesson.

establish

_____

_____

issue

_____

_____

Sum It Up

Why did the Romans see the Christians as traitors?

_____

_____

_____

_____

The Early Church (pages 513–514)

Scanning

Glance quickly over the reading to complete the chart below.

Hierarchy of the Clergy

Copyright © by The McGraw-Hill Companies, Inc.

Terms To Know

Define or describe the following terms from this lesson.

hierarchy

_____
_____

clergy

_____
_____

laity

_____
_____

doctrine

_____
_____

gospel

_____
_____

pope

_____
_____

Academic Vocabulary

Define this academic vocabulary word from this lesson.

unify

_____
_____

Sum It Up

What are the gospels, and why are they significant?

_____
_____
_____
_____

Copyright © by The McGraw-Hill Companies, Inc.

Key Points

Section Wrap-up

Now that you have read the section, write the answers to the questions that were included in **Setting a Purpose for Reading** *at the beginning of the lesson.*

How did Christianity become the official religion of the Roman Empire?

_____

_____

_____

_____

_____

_____

How was the early Christian Church organized?

_____

_____

_____

_____

_____

_____

Read To Write Challenge

Research the Christian martyr Perpetua. On a separate sheet of paper, write a **narrative essay** *describing who she was and why she chose martyrdom.*

Copyright © by The McGraw-Hill Companies, Inc.

Chapter 11, Section 3
The Spread of Christian Ideas

(Pages 515–521)

Main Idea

Setting a Purpose for Reading Think about these questions as you read:
- How did church and government work together in the Byzantine Empire?
- How did Christian ideas spread to Europe?

Reading Strategy

As you read pages 516–521 in your textbook, complete this diagram to show the reach of Christian missionaries.

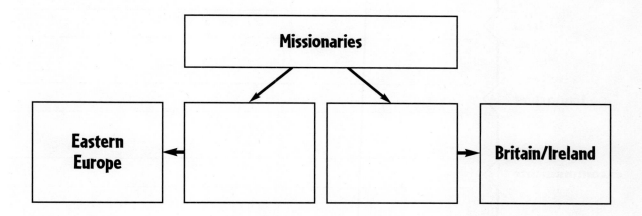

Copyright © by The McGraw-Hill Companies, Inc.

The Byzantine Church (pages 516–518)

Summarizing

As you read, look for the reasons for the conflicts that led up to the break between the Roman Catholic and Eastern Orthodox Churches. Then, after you read, use the chart below to summarize the major reasons for the split.

```
                    ┌─────────────────
                   ╱
┌──────────────┐  ╱ ─────────────────
│ Church Conflicts │◄
└──────────────┘  ╲ ─────────────────
                   ╲
                    └─────────────────
```

Terms To Know

Define or describe the following terms from this lesson.

icon > _____

_____

iconoclast > _____

_____

excommunicate > _____

_____

schism > _____

_____

Copyright © by The McGraw-Hill Companies, Inc.

People To Meet

Explain why this person is important.

Charlemagne

_____

_____

Places To Locate

Briefly describe the following place.

Byzantine Empire

_____

_____

Academic Vocabulary

Define this academic vocabulary word from this lesson.

survive

_____

_____

Sum It Up

How did the church and government work together in the Byzantine Empire?

_____

_____

_____

_____

_____

Copyright © by The McGraw-Hill Companies, Inc.

Christian Ideas Spread (pages 518–521)

Sequencing   *As you read, number the following events in the correct order.*

1. _____ Patrick brings Christianity to Ireland.

2. _____ Cyril invents a new Slavic alphabet.

3. _____ Paula builds churches, a hospital, and a convent in Palestine.

4. _____ Monks band together into the first monasteries.

5. _____ Pope Gregory I sends monks to take Christianity to England.

Terms To Know   *Define or describe the following terms from this lesson.*

monastery _____
_____
_____

missionary _____
_____

People To Meet   *Explain why these people are important.*

Cyril _____
_____

Patrick _____
_____
_____

Copyright © by The McGraw-Hill Companies, Inc.

 **Key Points**

 **Notes**

Places To Locate *Briefly describe the following places.*

Britain

_____

_____

Ireland

_____

_____

Sum It Up *Why were Basil and Benedict important?*

_____

_____

_____

_____

_____

Copyright © by The McGraw-Hill Companies, Inc.

 Notes

Section Wrap-up

Now that you have read the section, write the answers to the questions that were included in **Setting a Purpose for Reading** *at the beginning of the lesson.*

How did church and government work together in the Byzantine Empire?

_____

_____

_____

_____

_____

_____

How did Christian ideas spread to Europe?

_____

_____

_____

_____

_____

_____

Read To Write Challenge

Research the daily lives of early monks. On a separate sheet of paper, write an **expository paragraph** *explaining the series of activities monks did each day.*

Copyright © by The McGraw-Hill Companies, Inc.

Answer Key

CHAPTER 1, SECTION 1

Reading Strategy

Possible answers include:

Cause	Effect
hunters and gatherers	lived as nomads
cold climate	lived in caves, created new shelters
discovery of fire	warmth, safety, ability to cook
ability to farm	villages, communities, trade, specialization

Early Humans

Visualizing

Student answers will vary. Words and phrases may include tools and weapons made of stone; hunting and gathering; living as nomads; women at campsite; men hunting; living in caves; using fire for warmth, safety, and cooking; living in Ice Age; cave paintings; tools made with flint. Paragraphs should build on these images to create a visual picture of the life of early humans.

Terms to Know

anthropologist: person who studies how humans develop and relate to one another over time; archaeologist: person who digs up and studies things made by humans in the past; artifact: an object made by humans in the past, such as weapons or tools; fossil: traces of plants or animals that have been preserved in rock; nomad: people who live regularly moving from one place to another; technology: tools and methods to help perform tasks

Academic Vocabulary

task: a piece of work or job that must be done

Sum It Up

Fossils show signs of plant or animal life preserved in rock. Artifacts are weapons, tools, or other things made by humans.

The Agricultural Revolution

Inferring

Student webs will vary. Possible answers include: people could live in one place; people began to build villages; people developed communities with places of worship; healthy, growing populations; beginning of trade; developed different kinds of jobs; crafts developed; tools improved.

Terms to Know

domesticate: to train animals or plants for human use; specialization: the development of different kinds of jobs

Places to Locate

Jericho: one of the oldest communities, located in the Middle East

Academic Vocabulary

revolution: major changes that affect many different areas of life

Sum It Up

In Paleolithic times, people lived life as hunters and gatherers moving from place to place. In Neolithic times, people developed farming, communities, trade, and specialized jobs.

Section Wrap-Up

- They lived as nomads as they searched for food to eat, and they lived in caves to keep warm.
- People learned how to farm, so they could live in one place. Villages and communities developed, along with trade, specialized jobs, and more sophisticated tools.

Read to Write Challenge

Comparative essays should describe advantages of more calories, ability to feed more people, emergence of settled societies leading to organized civilizations. Disadvantages should include diets that changed from meat and vegetables to grains, spread of diseases, and polluted environments.

CHAPTER 1, SECTION 2

Reading Strategy

Second box: Conflict weakens Sumer's city-states and they are attacked.
Third box: Sargon conquers all of Mesopotamia and sets up the world's first empire.

Mesopotamia's Civilization

Outlining

I. Why Were River Valleys Important?
   A. Good farming conditions made it easy to feed large numbers of people.
   B. Rivers made it easier to develop trade.
II. The Rise of Sumer
   A. The earliest known civilization located on a flat plan between the Tigris River and the Euphrates River.
   B. Flooding left rich soil for farming and led to development of irrigation.
III. What Were City-States?
   A. Isolation of cities led to the development of separate city-states that had their own independent government.
   B. Sumerian city-states often went to war against each other.
IV. Gods and Rulers
   A. Sumerians believed in many gods.
   B. The priests and priestesses of the grand temple, or ziggurat, were very powerful.
V. What Was Life Like in Sumer?
   A. Most people lived in small mud-brick houses and farmed. Some were artisans and traders.
   B. People were divided into three social classes.

Terms to Know

civilization: a culture or society developed by a particular group of people; irrigation: way of watering crops that involves building walls and ditches to bring water to fields; city-state: separate and independent cities that had their own governments; artisan: skilled workers or craftspeople that make fabric, pottery, or other products

Places to Locate:

Tigris River: river in present-day southern Iraq; boundary for Mesopotamia; Euphrates River: river in present-day southern Iraq; boundary for Mesopotamia; Mesopotamia: area of the earliest known civilization, located between the Tigris and Euphrates Rivers; Sumer: region in southern Mesopotamia with many cities

Academic Vocabulary

complex: involved, intricate, or complicated

Sum It Up

They built irrigation systems.

A Skilled People

Drawing Conclusions

Student answers will vary. Details may include: They invented writing; they produced works of literature; they developed irrigation systems, wagon wheels, the plow, and the sailboat; they developed mathematical ideas; they studied the planets and stars and developed a calendar. The general statement should reflect a conclusion based on the details listed.

Terms to Know

cuneiform: Sumerian writing; scribe: record keeper

Academic Vocabulary

consist: to be made up or composed of

Terms to Review

Sample sentences:
Archaeologists learn about a society from its artifacts.
We depend on computer technology to e-mail friends.

Sum It Up

Sumerians used geometry to measure fields and put up buildings; they developed a number system based on 60, which led to the 60-minute hour and the 360-degree circle.

Sargon and Hammurabi

Summarizing

1. Sumeria was conquered by the Akkadians. Their king, Sargon, set up the world's first empire.
2. The Babylonian king Hammurabi is best known for his collection of laws. While some of his laws seem cruel, they were an important step toward a fair system of justice.

Answer Key

209

Terms to Know

empire: a large group of many different lands under one ruler

Places to Locate

Babylon: a city located on the Euphrates River that became powerful in Mesopotamia

People to Meet

Sargon: king of the Akkadians who established the world's first empire; Hammurabi: Babylonian king who established a system of laws

Academic Vocabulary

code: a collection or system of laws

Sum It Up

It was the first empire, conquering all of Mesopotamia and lasting more than 200 years.

Section Wrap-Up

- Good farming conditions along river valleys made it easy to feed large numbers of people; transportation along rivers increased trade, which led to the exchange of goods and ideas; cities developed and became centers of civilization.
- They invented writing; they produced works of literature; they developed irrigation systems, wagon wheels, the plow, and the sailboat; they developed mathematical ideas; they studied the planets and stars and developed a calendar.
- Conflicts between the city-states weakened Sumeria. They became vulnerable to attacks by outside groups. Eventually, Sargon conquered Mesopotamia.

Read to Write Challenge

Persuasive essays should list three of Hammurabi's laws with an explanation why each would benefit American society. Students may refer to pages 140-141 of the textbook for sample laws.

CHAPTER 1, SECTION 3

Reading Strategy

Assyrians: built strong, fierce army; established powerful, well-organized government; built road system; produced and collected literature

Chaldeans: built richest and largest city; built Hanging Gardens; rich from trade

Both: powerful empires in Mesopotamia; built large temples and palaces; made contributions to science

The Assyrians

Questioning

Student questions will vary. Questions should be based on main ideas in the text, including the strength of the Assyrian army, the organization of the government, and life in Assyria. Students should supply answers to their questions.

Terms to Know

province: a political district

Places to Locate

Assyria: empire in Mesopotamia that emerged around 900 B.C.; Persian Gulf: body of water located in the eastern part of the Assyrian Empire; Nineveh: capital of Assyria

Academic Vocabulary

core: the center or most important part

Sum It Up

They fought fiercely, set fire to captured cities, and carried away the city's people and goods.

The Chaldeans

Determining the Main Idea

Student answers will vary. They should address the beauty of the city of Babylon, life in Babylon, and the fall of Babylon.

Terms to Know

caravan: a group of traveling merchants; astronomer: person who studies the stars and planets

Places to Locate

Hanging Gardens: huge terraced gardens built by Nebuchadnezzar

People to Meet

Nebuchadnezzar: king of Chaldean Empire

Academic Vocabulary

interval: the space between two objects or points; route: a road or way to travel from one place to another

Sum It Up

Terraced gardens that featured large trees, flowering vines, and plants. They were considered one of the Seven Wonders of the Ancient World.

Section Wrap-Up

- To defend itself, it built a large and powerful army. It also established a well-organized government.
- It built a magnificent city featuring the Hanging Gardens of Babylon. It was a center of science. The Chaldeans made one of the first sundials and were the first to have a seven-day week.

Read to Write Challenge

Students' expository paragraphs should mention the well-organized government of the Assyrians, the construction of roads protected by soldiers, the architectural skill of builders, and the appreciation Assyrians had for knowledge and literature.

CHAPTER 2, SECTION 1

Reading Strategy

Possible answers include:

    Dug basins to trap floodwaters
    Dug canals to carry water to fields
    Built dikes to strengthen basin walls
    Used a shadoof to lift water from the Nile to the basins

Settling the Nile

Determining the Main Idea

Student notes should include a description of the Nile, the cataracts, the surrounding deserts, the delta marshes, and the sea borders. The following elements helped protect the Egyptians: the cataracts, the surrounding deserts, and the delta marshes.

Terms to Know

cataract: fast-moving water, rapids; delta: area of fertile soil that often surrounds the mouth of a river

Places to Locate

Egypt: civilization that developed in the Nile River valley; Nile River: world's longest river, flowing from central Africa to the Mediterranean Sea; Sahara: world's largest desert

Academic Vocabulary

feature: special part or quality that stands out

Terms to Review

Sample sentences:

The Egyptian civilization grew because it was protected from invaders.

Mesopotamian city-states were very independent and often fought one another.

Sum It Up

It was beautiful and lush. The Nile provided life, including fish, plants, and animals. The Nile ran through a narrow green valley surrounded by desert. Cataracts to the south and delta marshes to the north protected the area. Bordered to the north and east by seas, Egypt had access to trade routes.

The River People

Questioning

Student questions should address the main points in the section. Questions may include: How did flooding affect the Egyptians? How did the Egyptians use the Nile? What were hieroglyphics? Students should use facts from their reading to answer their questions.

Terms to Know

papyrus: reed plant that grew along the Nile and used to make baskets, sandals, rafts, and paper; hieroglyphics: Egyptian system of writing made up of symbols

Academic Vocabulary

technology: scientific knowledge used to develop tools, crafts, etc.

Terms to Review

Sample sentences:

Irrigation helped Egyptian farmers grow enough food to feed themselves and their animals.

Technology gives us new and better ways of working.

Sum It Up

When the flood water went down, it left behind dark, fertile soil.

A United Egypt
Drawing Conclusions
Students' notes may include the following facts: Narmer was able to lead his army and take control of Lower Egypt; Narmer ruled from Memphis, located on the border of the two kingdoms; Narmer wore a crown to symbolize unity; Narmer's kingdom held together long after his death. Conclusions will vary but should address how Narmer was able to successfully lead and unify the two kingdoms.

Terms to Know
dynasty: a line or series of rulers from the same family

Sum It Up
Narmer, the king of Upper Egypt in 3100 B.C., took control of Lower Egypt by force and unified the kingdoms.

Early Egyptian Life
Summarizing
1. pharaoh
2. nobles, priests, and army commanders
3. ran businesses or produced goods
4. farmers and unskilled workers
5. unskilled workers
6. women

Sum It Up
by upper-, middle-, and lower-class people

Section Wrap-Up
- Early Egyptians settled along the Nile River because the surrounding land was dry and received little rainfall. The river provided water for farming, drinking, bathing, as well as a source of fish and plants for food.
- The Nile and the surrounding area provided excellent land for farming, access to trade routes, and protection from invaders. In all this, it provided a land where the Egyptian people and culture could grow and prosper.
- Egyptian life was based on a highly structured social system. The highest classes lived with great wealth. Lower classes lived very simple lives. Most workers were artisans, traders, farmers, or unskilled. Fathers headed the home, but women also had rights. Girls were taught household duties. Boys were taught a trade. Few children went to school.

Read to Write Challenge
Students' essays should mention alphabet signs, syllabic signs, word signs, and determinatives. Refer students to page 11 of *Chapter 2 Resources* for further information.

CHAPTER 2, SECTION 2
Reading Strategy
Answers may include:
  Worshiped many gods and goddesses
  Deities control nature and humans

Main god was the sun god Re
Most important goddess was Isis
Lead good life and know magic spells to achieve life after death
Embalm pharaohs for the afterlife

Old Kingdom Rulers
Determining the Main Idea
Egypt was ruled by powerful kings called pharaohs.

Terms to Know
pharaoh: an Egyptian king

Academic Vocabulary
period: a specific amount or segment of time; welfare: health, happiness, and prosperity

Sum It Up
The people believed that the unity of their kingdom depended on strong leadership. They also thought pharaohs were gods on Earth who controlled their well-being.

Egypt's Religion
Previewing
Student answers will vary. Answers may focus on the Egyptian gods, life after death, embalming, and medicine.

Terms to Know
deity: a god or a goddess; embalming: the process of protecting and preserving a dead body; mummy: a body wrapped after death for protection

Sum It Up
Re, Hapi, Isis, and Osiris

The Pyramids
Inferring
Student answers should be based on their reading about Egypt and the pyramids. Their answers may relate to the importance and supremacy of the pharaoh, as well as the skill and knowledge of the people.

Terms to Know
pyramid: gigantic tomb with four triangular sides built in ancient Egypt

People to Meet
King Khufu: Egyptian king entombed in the Great Pyramid

Places to Locate
Giza: location on the Nile of the Great Pyramid

Academic Vocabulary
structure: something constructed, a building; principle: a basic rule or standard

Sum It Up
Pyramids were built to house and protect dead pharaohs.

Section Wrap-Up
- Egyptians believed in many gods and in life after death. They believed that the pharaoh was like a god and had ultimate authority.

- The pyramids were tombs for the pharaohs. They protected the dead bodies and held supplies for the afterlife.

Read to Write Challenge
Students' narrative paragraphs should sequence the steps involved in embalming. Refer students to page 15 of *Chapter 2 Resources* for further information.

CHAPTER 2, SECTION 3
Reading Strategy
Possible answers include:
  Battled to regain lands
  Rebuilt the empire
  Built many temples

The Middle Kingdom
Skimming
Student answers should include various aspects of the golden age, including increased land, increased wealth, and growth in the arts, literature, and architecture.

Terms to Know
tribute: forced payments

Places to Locate
Thebes: capital of Egypt established during the Middle Kingdom

People to Meet
Ahmose: Egyptian prince who drove the Hyksos out of Egypt

Academic Vocabulary
restore: to bring back to the original condition

Sum It Up
Tombs were painted with colorful scenes, sculptors carved images of pharaohs, poets wrote tributes to the pharaohs, and the cliff tombs of the Valley of the Kings were created.

The New Kingdom
Evaluating
Hatshepsut: first woman to rule in her own right; focused on trade instead of conquest; brought great wealth to Egypt; built monuments
Thutmose: fought aggressive wars to expand Egypt; grew rich through trade and tribute; enslaved many prisoners of war; rebuilt Thebes; made slavery common.
Student answers will vary. They should use the achievements of the leader they select to support their evaluations.

Terms to Review
Sample sentence: Egyptian pharaohs ruled as kings and gods over their people.

Sum It Up
Trade grew as they exchanged beads, metal tools, and weapons for ivory, wood, leopard skins, and incense.

Legacies of Two Pharaohs

Questioning
Student questions should be based on the main ideas in the text, including Akhenaton's role as a religious reformer and Tutankhamen's role as a boy king.

People to Meet
Akhenaton: pharaoh who created a new religion to limit the power of the priests

Academic Vocabulary
maintain: to keep in the same condition

Sum It Up
Tutankhamen's tomb contains many treasures to study. Most royal Egyptian tombs were robbed of all their treasures years ago.

The End of the New Kingdom

Sequencing
_4_ Groups from the eastern Mediterranean attack Egypt by sea.
_2_ Egyptian armies regain lands in western Asia.
_7_ Egypt is taken over by the Assyrians.
_5_ Egypt is conquered by Libyans.
_1_ Ramses II becomes pharaoh.
_6_ Egypt is ruled by Kush.
_3_ The temple at Karnak is built.

People to Meet
Ramses II: Egyptian pharaoh who reigned during the New Kingdom

Academic Vocabulary
construct: to make or build

Sum It Up
Outside groups with iron weapons conquered Egypt.

Section Wrap-Up
• The Middle Kingdom was a golden age. The kingdom enjoyed great wealth and an increase in the arts.
• Hatshepsut, Thutmose III, and Ramses II ruled as powerful pharaohs. All three expanded the wealth and power of the kingdom. Akhenaton introduced a new religion to help him retain power, but ultimately Egypt lost power during his reign. After Ramses II, Egypt's power began to fade and Egypt fell to outside invaders.

Read to Write Challenge
Students' paragraphs may mention Thutmose's soldiers hiding in baskets or how they carried boats overland to reach the Euphrates River.

Chapter 2, Section 4

Reading Strategy
Napata: no iron resources or weapons
Meroë: iron resources; became center for making iron
Both: capital cities with access for trade and transportation; built temples, monuments, and pyramids like those in Egypt

Nubia

Determining the Main Idea
Nubians settled south of Egypt and became strong warriors and wealthy traders who adopted many Egyptian ways.

Terms to Know
savanna: grassy plain

Places to Locate
Nubia: region south of Egypt along the Nile River where a strong civilization developed; Kush: name of region first known as Nubia; Kerma: wealthy Nubian kingdom

Academic Vocabulary
collapse: to fall suddenly

Terms to Review
Sample sentence:
Egyptians used hieroglyphics to communicate with symbols.

Sum It Up
to the south of Egypt along the Nile River, in present-day Sudan

The Rise of Kush

Outlining
I. The Importance of Iron
  A. The Kushites became the first Africans to devote themselves to ironworking.
  B. The use of iron increased the Kushites' military power.
II. A New Capital
  A. Kush rulers moved the capital to Meroë to move farther from the Assyrians.
  B. Meroë became a trading city and a center for ironmaking.
III. Building a Profitable Trade
  A. Meroë became the center of a large trading network.
  B. Kush remained a trading power for about 600 years.

Places to Locate
Napata: early capital of Kush; Meroë: new capital of Kush established about 540 B.C.

People to Meet
Kashta: Kushite king who ruled over Egypt; Piye: son of Kashta who ruled both Egypt and Kush from Napata

Academic Vocabulary
decline: to move downward in condition, to fail

Terms to Review
Sample sentences:
People traveled together in caravans to sell their goods.
The family of rulers founded a dynasty that ruled Egypt and Kush.

Sum It Up
Kush became a wealthy kingdom through trade and ironmaking.

Section Wrap-Up
• These people lived south of Egypt along the Nile. They grew crops and were excellent hunters and fighters.
• Their kingdom grew wealthy from trade and iron making. As a people, they adopted many Egyptian ways and built many monuments, temples, and pyramids in the fashion of the Egyptians.

Read to Write Challenge
Students' essays should include quotes from Scottish explorer James Bruce, who sighted the ruins in 1772.

Chapter 3, Section 1

Reading Strategy
Mesopotamia
Canaan
Egypt
Sinai Desert
Canaan

The Early Israelites

Connecting
Student answers will vary. Their paragraphs should reflect an understanding of Jewish beliefs and make specific connections with personal or cultural religious, ethical, and moral values.

Terms to Know
monotheism: belief in one god; tribe: a unit of society made up of family groups; Torah: Jewish religious law; covenant: a formal agreement

People to Meet
Abraham: the father of the Israelites; Jacob: grandson of Abraham and father of the 12 tribes of Israel; Moses: man who led the Israelites out of slavery in Egypt

Academic Vocabulary
focus: to look toward a single point or purpose; occupy: to dwell or live in

Terms to Review
Sample sentence: Egypt's pharaohs ruled as kings and gods.

Sum It Up
monotheism

The Promised Land

Responding
Student paragraphs will vary. Their responses should include thoughts and questions about the Israelites and about Joshua. Do they believe the story? Why or why not? What does this story reveal about the faith of the Israelites?

Terms to Know
alphabet: a group of letters that stands for sounds

People to Meet
Deborah: Israelite judge who defeated King Jabin and his army; Phoenicians: group of

Canaanites who lived in cities along the Mediterranean

Academic Vocabulary

create: to make, to bring into being

Terms to Review

Sample sentence: Israel consisted of 12 tribes or groups of family members.

Sum It Up

Joshua; Jericho

Section Wrap-Up

- They believed in one god and followed the laws from the Torah, including the Ten Commandments.
- They returned to Canaan, their Promised Land, when God delivered them from slavery in Egypt.

Read to Write Challenge

Students' essays should include Terah, Abraham's father, and Nahor and Haran, Abraham's brothers. Essays should also list Abraham's eight sons.

CHAPTER 3, SECTION 2

Reading Strategy

Israel	Judah
North	South
Samaria	Jerusalem
772 B.C.	620 B.C.
Assyrians	Egyptians

The Israelites Choose a King

Determining the Main Idea

The Israelites chose a king to unite them against their enemies.

Terms to Know

prophet: person who claims to hear and speak words from God

People to Meet

Philistines: strongest people living in Canaan; enemies of the Israelites; Saul: Israel's first king; David: shepherd chosen by God to replace Saul as king

Academic Vocabulary

instruct: to teach, to direct

Sum It Up

They wanted a king to unite and lead them against their enemies, the Philistines.

David and Solomon

Summarizing

1. Goliath; slingshot; Saul; kill
2. 1000 B.C.; killed
3. Jerusalem; Solomon
4. Israel; Judah

Terms to Know

empire: a nation that rules several other nations; tribute: money or enslaved persons given to a stronger ruler; proverbs: wise sayings

Places to Locate

Jerusalem: the capital of Israel established by David, later became the capital of Judah; Judah: smaller kingdom that broke away from Israel, founded by two tribes in the south

Academic Vocabulary

symbol: an image or object used to represent something else

Sum It Up

David built an Israelite empire and made Jerusalem his capital.

A Troubled Time

Sequencing

- _3_ The Egyptians conquer Judah.
- _5_ The Jews unite with the Egyptians to fight the Chaldeans.
- _6_ King Nebuchadnezzar captures Jerusalem.
- _1_ The Assyrians conquer Israel and scatter the 10 tribes.
- _7_ Nebuchadnezzar takes the Jews into captivity in Babylon.
- _2_ The Assyrians become known as Samaritans and eventually worship Israel's God.
- _4_ The Chaldeans conquer Egypt.

People to Meet

Nebuchadnezzar: Chaldean king who defeated Judah and captured Israel

Sum It Up

They were building their own empires in southwest Asia.

Section Wrap-Up

- Because they wanted a strong leader to unify them and protect them from their enemies.
- He is considered the greatest king of Israel. He conquered neighboring nations, created an empire, and established the capital of Jerusalem.
- The powerful Assyrians and Chaldeans threatened the weakened Israelites. They wanted to control the trade routes through Israel. The Israelites were conquered by the Assyrians in 722 B.C.

Read to Write Challenge

Students' essays should compare and contrast at least three prophets and their teachings. See page 211 of the textbook for further information.

CHAPTER 3, SECTION 3

Reading Strategy

Answers may include:

Led by priest named Judas Maccabeus
Rebelled against Antiochus and fled
Formed an army called the Maccabees
Drove the Greeks out of Judah and destroyed all traces of Greek gods in their temple

Restored their temple to worship of their God
Remembered in the celebration of Hanukkah
Became new rulers of Judah

Exile and Return

Outlining

I. Why Did Jews Return to Judah?
  A. The Persian king Cyrus allowed the Jews to return to Judah.
  B. Persians controlled the government, so Jews looked to their religion for leadership.
II. What Is in the Hebrew Bible?
  A. Thirty-nine books including Jewish history and the Torah.
  B. The Jews believed that God had a special role for them in history.
III. The Jews Look to the Future
  A. The Bible describes God's plans for a peaceful future.
  B. The Jews believed that good would ultimately triumph over evil.

Terms to Know

exile: forced removal from a native country; Sabbath: weekly day of worship and rest; synagogue: Jewish place of worship

Places to Locate

Babylon: the land of exile for the Jews

Academic Vocabulary

series: objects or events that come one after the other

Terms to Review

Sample sentence: A Jewish scribe named Ezra helped write the first five books of the Torah.

Sum It Up

Cyrus allowed the Jews to return to Judah.

The Jews and the Greeks

Questioning

Student questions should be based on the main ideas in the text, including the influence of the Greeks on the Jews, the Diaspora, the Maccabees, and Hanukkah.

Terms to Know

Diaspora: term referring to the scattered people of Israel

People to Meet

Judas Maccabeus: priest who led the rebellion against Antiochus and the new ruler of Judah

Academic Vocabulary

version: translation from another language; trace: visible evidence

Sum It Up

He introduced them to Greek language and culture. Jews who learned Greek translated the Hebrew Bible. This helped people who were not Jews understand Jewish history and ideas.

The Jewish Way of Life

Determining the Main Idea

Answers will vary, but may include:

Jewish law set out rules for living
Jews placed great importance on family
Education was very important, including
religious education for boys
Jews followed strict dietary laws
Jewish law forbade mixing some fabrics

Sum It Up

because they carried on the family name and
became head of the family upon the father's
death

The Jews and the Romans

Monitoring Comprehension

1. He was cruel. He made the temple very
   grand. He ruled when Jesus was born and
   he allowed Jewish rulers to run Judah.
2. They were splintered into different
   groups.
3. They taught the Torah and how to apply
   it to daily life.
4. They were priests and scribes concerned
   with the law in the Temple.
5. They were priests who broke away from
   the temple and lived in the desert praying
   for God's deliverance.
6. Jewish hatred of the Romans led to the
   revolts. The revolts led to the death of
   thousands, the destruction of the temple,
   and exile. The Romans renamed Judah
   Palestine.
7. Rabbis were teachers of the Torah who
   held an important place in Jewish society.
   They developed the Talmud to pass on
   teachings about the Torah.

Terms to Know

messiah: a deliverer sent by God; rabbi:
teacher of Jewish law

People to Meet

Herod: Roman king who ruled over Judea;
Zealots: Jews who wanted to fight the
Romans for their freedom; Johanan ben
Zakkai: Jewish rabbi who founded a school
in northern Palestine that became a center
of Torah studies

Sum It Up

Ultimately, it resulted in loss of Jewish lives,
as well as their homeland and temple.

Section Wrap-Up

- Jews who were scattered to other lands
  learned Greek and translated their Bible
  so that other people could learn about
  Jewish ideas.
- The Jews hated Roman rule and revolted.

Read to Write Challenge

Students' essays should describe Esther's role
in the festival of Purim as well as the four
mitzvahs of listening to the Megillah, giving
to charity, giving two kinds of snacks, and
having fun.

CHAPTER 4, SECTION 1

Reading Strategy

Made cattle sacred; improved farming; developed the Sanskrit language; caste system

The Land of India

Evaluating

1. Fact: the list of conveniences. Opinion:
   the conclusion that the city government
   was well organized.
2. Fact: the location of the palace and the
   temple. Opinion: the conclusion that religion and politics were closely connected.

Terms to Know

subcontinent: a very large area of land that is
part of a continent but is independent
because it is separated by geography or politics; monsoon: strong wind that blows one
direction in winter and the opposite direction in summer

Academic Vocabulary

similar: alike in appearance or nature

Terms to Review

Sample sentence: Archaeologists learned a lot
about early Indian civilization from the ruins
at Harappa.

Sum It Up

Snow melt from the Himalaya feed rivers that
flood and leave behind fertile farmland.

The Aryans Invade

Summarizing

Facts listed should include: Aryans raised cattle; cattle were prized because they provided
meat, milk, and butter; cattle were used as
money; Aryans made cattle sacred

Terms to Know

Sanskrit: Aryan written language; raja: prince
who led an Aryan tribe

Academic Vocabulary

individual: relating to one person

Terms to Review

Sample sentences:
People who were nomads like the Aryans
moved from place to place.
The Aryans lived in tribes, or groups made up
of family members.

Sum It Up

They forbid cattle from being used as food
and improved farming with iron tools; they
constructed canals and brought Sanskrit to
India.

Society in Ancient India

Connecting

Student answers will vary. Students should
reflect on personal experiences of discrimination, then examine the effects of discrimination in the world today.

Terms to Know

caste: a social group that someone is born
into and cannot change; guru: a teacher

Sum It Up

Brahmans (priests), Kshatriyas (warriors,
rulers), Vaisyas (commoners), Sudras
(unskilled workers, servants), and Pariahs
(Untouchables)

Section Wrap-Up

- Geography (mountains) and climate
  (rivers, monsoons) influenced the rise of
  India's first civilization.
- They introduced many new ideas including improved farming, the Sanskrit language, and the caste system.

Read to Write Challenge

Students' paragraphs may include family
pressure, tradition, caste system, and fear
of persecution.

CHAPTER 4, SECTION 2

Reading Strategy

Universal spirit called Brahman; karma; reincarnation; dharma or divine law

Hinduism

Synthesizing

Student answers will vary. Students should
write about the basic beliefs of Hinduism
including Brahman, karma, reincarnation, and
dharma or divine law. They should also
reflect on how their beliefs give them hope
for life in a better caste if they do their duty
in this life.

Terms to Know

Hinduism: religion that began with the
Aryans; includes beliefs about karma, reincarnation, and dharma; Brahman: the Hindu
universal spirit; reincarnation: the idea of
passing through many lives to reach Brahman;
dharma: divine law that requires people to
do the duties of the caste; karma: the conse-
quences of how a person lives

Academic Vocabulary

affect: to cause a change in; to influence;
require: to demand or compel

Terms to Review

Sample sentence:
Aryan beliefs were written down over the
years in the language of Sanskrit.

Sum It Up

The Aryans' beliefs changed after borrowing
religious beliefs from the people they conquered in India, and these mixed beliefs
became Hinduism.

Buddhism

Scanning

1. the founder of Buddhism, Siddhartha
   Gautama
2. a state of wisdom reached when people
   give up all desires
3. the Four Noble Truths and the Eightfold
   Path

4. Theravada Buddhism and Mahayana Buddhism
5. the Buddhist leader who headed the government in Tibet

Terms to Know
Buddhism: religion founded by Siddhartha Gautama that includes the Four Noble Truths and Eightfold Path; nirvana: state of wisdom reached when a person gives up all desires; theocracy: government headed by religious leaders

Academic Vocabulary
area: a defined space, part, or section; aware: having knowledge of something

Sum It Up
through the travel and teaching of the Buddha's disciples

Section Wrap-Up
- Hinduism is a religion founded by Aryans that includes beliefs about karma, reincarnation, and dharma.
- Buddhism was founded by Siddhartha Gautama and includes beliefs about nirvana, Four Noble Truths, and the Eightfold Path.

Read to Write Challenge
Students' essays may note that the Ten Commandments (on page 203 of the textbook) list actions NOT to do, whereas the Eightfold Path (on page 250) also lists actions that people SHOULD do.

CHAPTER 4, SECTION 3
Reading Strategy
Dates:
  321 B.C. empire is founded
  273 B.C. to 232 B.C. Asoka rules
  183 B.C. last ruler is killed
Capital:
  Pataliputra
Government:
  dynasty; centralized government

The Mauryan Dynasty
Inferring
Possible answers include:
  Dedicated life to peace and Buddhism
  Built new roads with shelters and shade
  Built hospitals
  Sent Buddhist teachers throughout India and Asia
  Practiced tolerance

Terms to Know
dynasty: series of rulers from the same family; stupa: Buddhist shrines in the shape of a dome

Places to Locate
Pataliputra: capital city of the Mauryan dynasty

People to Meet
Chandragupta Maurya: founder of India's first empire, the Mauryan dynasty

Sum It Up
He was a strong military leader but was also dedicated to peace and Buddhism. He built roads and hospitals. He spread Buddhist teachings but practiced tolerance. With a good road system and a strong ruler, the empire prospered.

The Gupta Empire
Determining the Main Idea
Student answers will vary. Generally, they should focus on the fact that the Gupta empire reunited much of northern India and became wealthy through trade.

Terms to Know
pilgrim: a person who travels to a religious shrine or site

Academic Vocabulary
dominate: to control or rule by the use of power

Sum It Up
through trade and pilgrims who traveled to visit shrines

Indian Literature and Science
Reviewing
Literature: Vedas; *Mahabharata; Ramayana; Bhagavad Gita; The Cloud Messenger*
Math: algebra; the idea of zero; the concept of infinity; symbols for 1–9; algorithms
Science: astronomy; Earth revolves around sun; gravity; atoms; set broken bones; performed operations; invented medical tools; plastic surgery

People to Meet
Kalidasa: India's best-known author; wrote the poem *The Cloud Messenger*

Academic Vocabulary
concept: an idea, thought, or plan

Sum It Up
astronomy; mathematics; medicine

Section Wrap-Up
- India's first great empires were the Mauryan and Gupta empires.
- These empires contributed great works of literature as well as advances in math and science, including the idea of zero, the concept of infinity, symbols for 1–9, algorithms, astronomy, and medicine.

Read to Write Challenge
Students' essays should incorporate an Indian fable along with a summary of the fable's moral lesson.

CHAPTER 5, SECTION 1
Reading Strategy
Shang
Dates: 1750 B.C. to 1045 B.C.
Leadership: King ruled; chose warlords to govern the territories

Accomplishments: produced silk; made vases and dishes from white clay; carved statues from ivory and jade; made bronze works

Zhou
Dates: 1045 B.C. to 221 B.C.
Leadership: Kings ruled with a large bureaucracy; put aristocrats in charge of territories
Accomplishments: irrigation and flood-control systems; iron plows; silk trade

China's Geography
Monitoring Comprehension
Effect: Destruction; rich soil for farming
Effect: Little land for farming; separation from other peoples

Places to Locate
Huang He: flows across China for 2,900 miles from Mongolia to Pacific Ocean; Chang Jiang: flows 3,400 miles east across central China to the Yellow Sea

Sum It Up
Huang He and Chang Jiang

The Shang Dynasty
Outlining
I. Who Were the Shang?
  A. The Shang may have built the first Chinese cities.
  B. Warlords governed the territories.
  C. Warlords and royal officials made up the upper class of aristocrats.
  D. Most people were farmers.
II. Spirits and Ancestors
  A. The Shang worshiped gods and spirits.
  B. People honored their ancestors.
III. Telling the Future
  A. Religion and government were closely linked.
  B. The kings asked for the gods' help by using oracle bones.
IV. The Chinese Language
  A. Chinese writing uses pictographs and ideographs.
  B. Most Chinese characters represent whole words.
V. Shang Artists
  A. Shang people produced silk, vases, dishes, and statues.
  B. The Shang are best known for their works in bronze.

Terms to Know
dynasty: a line of rulers who belong to the same family; aristocrat: noble or member of the ruling class; pictograph: characters that stand for objects; ideograph: characters that join two or more pictographs to represent an idea

Places to Locate
Anyang: the first capital city of China; Shang kings ruled from here

Academic Vocabulary
recover: to get back or restore to a normal state; interpret: to explain the meaning of

Terms to Review

Sample sentences:
Pottery and other artifacts helped archaeologists find the first center of Chinese civilization.
Kings and priests used oracle bones to receive messages from the gods.

Sum It Up

They governed the kingdom's territories.

The Zhou Dynasty

Questioning

Student questions will vary. Questions should be based on main ideas in the text, including the Zhou government, the Mandate of Heaven, new tools and trade, and the fall of the Zhou empire.

Terms to Know

bureaucracy: the officials and their areas or departments of government; mandate: a formal order; Dao: the proper "Way" to keep the gods happy

People to Meet

Wu Wang: aristocrat who overthrew the Shang and started the Zhou dynasty

Academic Vocabulary

link: a point of connection; item: a single unit or part

Terms to Review

Sample sentence: The Chinese developed irrigation during the Zhou dynasty to move water to areas for farming.

Sum It Up

by claiming a heavenly law gave them the right to rule

Section Wrap-Up

- Geography (rivers, mountains, and deserts) helped shape China's first civilization. It developed in the Huang He valley. The rich soil there was great for farming. As their numbers grew, people began building towns. Soon after, the first Chinese civilization began.
- Zhou rulers said a heavenly law, the Mandate of Heaven, gave them power to rule.

Read to Write Challenge

Students should explain that pictographs represent objects whereas ideographs join together pictographs to represent an idea. Students' names will vary.

CHAPTER 5, SECTION 2

Reading Strategy

Top: aristocrats
Middle: farmers
Bottom: merchants

Life in Ancient China

Skimming

Student answers may include: aristocrats relied on farmers to grow the crops that made them rich; landowners and farmers looked down on merchants; Chinese leaders believed that government officials should not be concerned with money, so merchants could not hold government jobs; men were respected because they grew crops.

Terms to Know

social class: a group of people who share a similar position in society; filial piety: the practice of showing respect to parents and older relatives

Academic Vocabulary

convince: to persuade

Sum It Up

Aristocrats divided their land among their sons.

Chinese Thinkers

Summarizing

Confucius: Confucius taught that people needed to have a sense of duty. His philosophy taught that people must also be good and seek knowledge.
Laozi: Daoism is based on the teachings of Laozi. This philosophy taught that people should give up worldly desires, turn to nature, and follow the force that guides all things (the Dao).
Hanfeizi: Legalism is based on the teachings of Hanfeizi. This philosophy taught that people are evil and need a system of laws to make them do their duty.

Terms to Know

Confucianism: Chinese philosophy that taught that people must do their duty to others to improve society; Daoism: Chinese philosophy that says people should give up worldly desires and turn to nature and the Dao; Legalism: Chinese philosophy that taught that people are evil and need harsh laws to make them do their duty

Academic Vocabulary

promote: to advance; to further the progress of

Sum It Up

He believed that all people were naturally evil.

Section Wrap-Up

- Ancient Chinese society was organized into three social classes: aristocrats, farmers, and merchants.
- Chinese thinkers developed three major philosophies: Confucianism, Daoism, and Legalism.

Read to Write Challenge

Students' paragraphs should summarize one of Confucius's analects. Refer students to page 39 of *Chapter 5 Resources*.

CHAPTER 5, SECTION 3

Reading Strategy

Answers may include:
Waterwheels; grind more grain
Iron drill bits; mine more salt
Paper; record government information
Acupuncture; ease pain
Rudder; ships could sail into the wind, expanded trade

Emperor Qin Shihuangdi

Evaluating

Possible answers include:
Unified China
Made a strong central government
Created one currency
Built roads and canal
Built the Great Wall
Student evaluations will vary. In general, they should weigh his accomplishments against his methods. They should consider the qualities most important in a leader. Do his Legalism and cruelty make him a bad leader despite his accomplishments?

Academic Vocabulary

currency: a type of money; civil: of or relating to citizens

Sum It Up

He punished or killed anyone who opposed him.

The Han Dynasty

Monitoring Comprehension

1. The exams favored the rich because only they could afford to educate their sons for the exams.
2. Farmers had divided their land among their sons, leaving them with only about one acre of land. They had to sell their land to aristocrats and become tenant farmers.
3. Chinese merchants could travel farther. They expanded trade.

Terms to Know

acupuncture: practice of sticking needles into a person's skin to ease his or her pain

Academic Vocabulary

found: establish, set up, create; secure: free from danger or attack

Terms to Review

Sample sentences:
The government bureaucracy is made up of many levels and different jobs.
The aristocrats were nobles who owned land that was farmed by tenants.

Sum It Up

waterwheels, iron drill bits, steel, paper, acupuncture, rudder

The Silk Road

Determining the Main Idea

Student answers will vary. Generally, they should address the fact that the Silk Road carried Chinese goods as far as southwest Asia and the Mediterranean Sea.

Sum It Up
The trip was expensive because it was difficult and dangerous. Merchants had to pay taxes to kingdoms as they traveled.

Major Changes in China
Skimming
Answers may include the fall of the Han dynasty, growth of Buddhism in China, civil war, and invasion by northern nomads.

Sum It Up
merchants and scholars

Section Wrap-Up
• He used force and Legalism to control the country. He punished or killed anyone who opposed him.
• New inventions included waterwheels, iron drill bits, paper, acupuncture, and the rudder.

Read to Write Challenge
Students' narratives should include physical dangers—mountains, crossing rivers on camels, deserts, and narrow passages. The stories should also include the human dangers—bandits, greedy merchants, and government soldiers.

CHAPTER 6, SECTION 1

Reading Strategy

Olmec	Near present-day Vera Cruz, Mexico	1200 B.C. to 400 B.C.	Used rivers for trade, built planned city
Moche	Peru	A.D. 100 to A.D. 700	Used irrigation, farmed, hunted, fished, built huge pyramids, traded pottery, jewelry, and cloth

Farming in Mesoamerica
Analyzing
Glaciers melted and the land bridge to America disappeared
Some animals became extinct
Warm weather opened new opportunities to early Americans

Terms to Know
glacier: a huge sheet of ice

Places to Locate
Mesoamerica: "middle" America, region stretching from the Valley of Mexico to Costa Rica

Academic Vocabulary
expose: to reveal or make visible; estimate: to calculate approximately

Sum It Up
People discovered they could plant seeds and grow crops.

Early American Civilizations
Drawing Conclusions
Olmec: built big trading empire; Maya: traded throughout Mesoamerica; reached as far as southern Mexico and Central America; Moche: irrigated the land; designed huge pyramids; traded as far away as the Amazon River valley. Student general statements will vary. Generally, they should note that the civilizations developed trade, technology, and systems to rule large empires. They should speculate about the advanced level of these societies.

People to Meet
Olmec: one of the earliest Mesoamerican civilizations; built a large trading empire near present-day Vera Cruz, Mexico; Maya: early Mesoamerican civilization located on the Yucatán Peninsula; Moche: early Mesoamerican civilization located in present-day Peru; built huge pyramids

Places to Locate
Teotihuacan: "Place of the Gods"; the first planned city in the Americas, built by the Olmec

Terms to Review
Sample sentences:
The Olmec built a far-reaching trading empire. Moche engineers built huge pyramids to honor their gods.

Sum It Up
the Moche civilization; west coast of South America where Peru is today

Section Wrap-up
• by crossing a land bridge from Asia
• they were based on farming

Read to Write Challenge
Paragraphs should mention the shamans' role in the harvest, medicine, predicting future events, and so on.

CHAPTER 6, SECTION 2

Reading Strategy
Mayan achievements include: astronomy, calendar, mathematics, written language

The Mayan People
Previewing
Student answers will vary. Answers may focus on the concept of a civilization, city-states, Mesoamerica, and the rain forest.

Terms to Know
sinkholes: areas where the earth has collapsed

Places to Locate
Petén: "flat region" in present-day Guatemala; Tikal: Mayan city-state ruled by Jasaw Chan K'awiil I

People to Meet
Jasaw Chan K'awiil: Mayan ruler of the city-state Tikal

Academic Vocabulary
access: ability to make use of something

Sum It Up
The main advantage of living in a tropical rain forest was an adequate water supply.

Mayan Culture
Summarizing
1. god-kings; sun; captives; pyramid
2. heavens; 365-day calendar; hieroglyphics
3. 500; 900s

Terms to Know
alliance: political agreements between people or states to work together

Academic Vocabulary
predict: to tell or make known in advance

Sum It Up
Enslaved people were usually put to work, but sometimes were sacrificed to the Mayan gods.

Section Wrap-up
• The Maya created a civilization of city-states and lived in Mesoamerica's rain forest.
• The Maya developed a society of city-states and a culture based on their religion.

Read to Write Challenge
Students' essays should incorporate the story of clay and wooden men into their summaries.

CHAPTER 7, SECTION 1

Reading Strategy
Student answers will vary. Answers appearing in the organizer may include: created by nobles; made up of a town or city and the surrounding countryside; like a tiny independent country; main gathering place was the acropolis; included an agora; varied in size.

The Geography of Greece
Visualizing
Student answers will vary. Words and phrases may include: mountainous land; sparkling blue water; surrounded by seas; hundreds of islands; peninsula. Paragraphs should build on these images to create a visual picture of Greece.

Terms to Know
peninsula: a piece of land with water on three sides

Sum It Up
The mountains and seas divided Greek communities.

The Minoans
Questioning
Student questions will vary. They should address the main ideas in the text, including the discovery of Minoan civilization; the

palace at Knossos; trade; or the collapse of the civilization.

Academic Vocabulary
region: a large area

Places to Locate
Crete: an island southeast of the Greek mainland; center of Minoan civilization

Terms to Review
Sample sentences:
The archaeologist traveled to Greece to search for ancient relics.
The ancient civilization of Greece still influences our government today.

Sum It Up
They built ships and sailed to other countries, including Egypt and Syria.

The First Greek Kingdoms

Outlining
I. What Were Mycenaean Kingdoms Like?
  A. The center was a protected palace on a hill surrounded by farms.
  B. Artisans, workers, and government officials all worked in the palaces.
II. Power From Trade and War
  A. Mycenaeans learned from the Minoan culture.
  B. The Mycenaeans replaced the Minoans as the major power in the Mediterranean.
III. What Was the Dark Age?
  A. The Mycenaean civilization collapsed by 1100 B.C., and the Dark Age began.
  B. The Dorians invaded Greece, bringing more advanced technology, resulting in farming, trade, and a new alphabet.

People to Meet
Agamemnon: Mycenaean king who won the Trojan War

Places to Locate
Mycenae: the city in which a walled palace was discovered by Heinrich Schliemann; Peloponnesus: peninsula in southwest Greece

Academic Vocabulary
culture: traits, beliefs, and behaviors shared by a group of people; overseas: located across the sea

Terms to Review
Sample sentence:
Artisans in ancient Greek kingdoms made jars for wine and olive oil.

Sum It Up
The Mycenaeans learned about bronze, shipbuilding, and navigation from the Minoans and became great traders.

The Polis

Previewing
Student answers will vary. Answers may focus on the concept of the polis, the idea of Greek citizenship, or the role that citizens played as soldiers.

Terms to Know
polis: Greek city-state; agora: open area in a polis that served as a market and a place to meet and debate

Academic Vocabulary
community: a group of people living in the same place

Terms to Review
Sample sentence: Greek city-states were like tiny, independent countries.

Sum It Up
The Greeks were the first to treat a group of people (citizens) as equals who had rights and responsibilities. Other cultures treated most people as subjects with no rights.

A Move to Colonize

Determining the Main Idea
Student answers will vary. They should address the spread of Greek culture and increase in industry through colonies and trade.

Terms to Know
colony: settlement in a distant land that stays linked to its homeland

Sum It Up
The growth of trade between colonies and parent cities led to a growth in industry.

Section Wrap-Up
- The Mycenaeans built the first Greek kingdoms. They invaded the Greek mainland and conquered the people living there. They built palaces and developed trade as they spread their power across the Mediterranean region.
- They were the first to develop the idea of citizenship. They developed armies of ordinary citizens.

Read to Write Challenge
Students' essays should mention the Athenian hero Theseus, the half-bull/half-human Minotaur, King Minos, Daedalus, and Minos's daughter Ariadne.

CHAPTER 7, SECTION 2

Reading Strategy
Sparta: conquered and enslaved neighbors; controlling government; trained boys and men for war; girls were trained in sports; oligarchy; discouraged foreign visitors and travel; frowned upon study; fell behind in trade
Both: played key roles in defending Greece
Athens: set up colonies; valued education for boys; girls learned household duties; reforms led to democratic ideas; allowed male citizens to vote; included a council and assembly

Tyranny in the City-States

Summarizing
1. small farmers, merchants, artisans; tyrants; nobles
2. citizens; oligarchies; democracies

Terms to Know
tyrant: someone who takes power by force; oligarchy: government run by a few people; democracy: government in which power is held by the people

Places to Locate
Sparta: city-state with an oligarchy; Athens: city-state with a democracy

Sum It Up
Small farmers, merchants, and artisans wanted change. The tyrants could overthrow the nobles with the backing of the common people. They built new marketplaces, temples, and walls.

Sparta

Drawing Conclusions
Student answers will vary. Details may include: Spartans were conquerors; they enslaved their neighbors; they controlled the people; they trained boys and men for war; they trained girls in sports; their government was an oligarchy; they discouraged visitors and travel; they discouraged study. The general statement should reflect a conclusion based on the details listed.

Terms to Know
helots: workers captured by the Spartans

Academic Vocabulary
enforce: to make someone obey using force

Sum It Up
Spartans feared that the people they had captured might rebel.

Athens

Connecting
Student answers will vary. Paragraphs should compare democracy in the United States today with the democracy of Athens. Student answers should cite differences and similarities, including the assembly, the right to vote, the ability to debate, the council, and the lottery.

Academic Vocabulary
participate: to take part in something

People to Meet
Solon: Athenian leader who made reforms, allowed all male citizens to participate in the assembly; Peisistratus: tyrant who seized power in 560 B.C. and won support of the poor; Cleisthenes: reformed Athens's government, created a new council of 500 citizens to help the assembly carry out business

Sum It Up
He reorganized the assembly to play the central role in governing and created a new

council to help the assembly carry out daily business.

Section Wrap-Up

- They needed more land to grow, so they conquered and enslaved their neighbors. They used military force to keep the people they had conquered from rebelling.
- The Athenians valued learning as well as sport. Boys were educated. Girls learned household duties. Athenians also allowed citizens a voice in government.

Read to Write Challenge

Students' essays should exhibit persuasive techniques in trying to convert Spartans to become like Athenians, or vice versa.

CHAPTER 7, SECTION 3

Reading Strategy

Cyrus: united Persians into powerful kingdom; captured Babylon; treated all subjects well
Darius: reorganized government to make it work better; divided the empire into states; defeated in the Battle of Marathon
Xerxes: launched invasion of Greece to avenge his father

The Persian Empire

Outlining

I. The Rise of the Persian Empire
  A. Cyrus's armies conquered many lands to build an empire.
  B. Other leaders added territory and built miles of roads to connect their holdings.
II. What Was Persian Government Like?
  A. Darius reorganized the government to make it work better.
  B. The government paid full-time soldiers to protect the king's power.
III. The Persian Religion
  A. The Persian religion was called Zoroastrianism.
  B. Zoroaster believed in one god and taught that humans had the freedom to choose between good and evil.

Terms to Know

satrapies: states that formed the empire; satrap: an official who ruled a satrapy; Zoroastrianism: the religion of Persia

People to Meet

Cyrus the Great: leader who united the Persians into the largest empire in the world

Academic Vocabulary

vision: mystical experience of seeing the supernatural

Terms to Review

Sample sentences:
Hunters and gatherers were nomads because they had to move from place to place to find food.
Persia conquered many lands to build its great empire.

Sum It Up

The empire was very big and difficult to manage. King Darius divided the empire into 20 satrapies. Dividing it into smaller states made the government work better.

The Persian Wars

Sequencing

_5_ Greek army crushed the Persian army at Plataea.
_2_ Persian fleet landed 20,000 soldiers on the plain of Marathon.
_1_ Athenian army helped the Greeks in Asia Minor rebel against Persian rulers.
_4_ Xerxes launches invasion of Greece.
_6_ Alexander invades the Persian Empire.
_3_ Darius dies.

Places to Locate

Marathon: plain where the Persian army was defeated by the Greeks; Thermopylae: a narrow pass through the mountains where the Greeks fought bravely against the Persians; Salamis: a narrow strip of water where the Greeks destroyed almost the entire Persian fleet; Plataea: location of the battle where the Greeks crushed the Persian army, convincing the Persians to retreat

People to Meet

Xerxes: son of Darius who vowed revenge against the Athenians and launched a new invasion of Greece; Themistocles: Athenian general

Academic Vocabulary

internal: located inside

Sum It Up

The Athenian army helped the Greeks in Asia Minor rebel against their Persian rulers.

Section Wrap-Up

- Cyrus united the Persians into a powerful kingdom and sent armies to take over Mesopotamia, Asia Minor, Syria, Canaan, and the Phoenician cities. Cyrus's merciful rule helped hold the empire together.
- The Athenians defeated the Persians at the Battle of Marathon. Then the Athenians and Spartans united to defeat the Persians when Xerxes launched an invasion. Sparta sent the most soldiers. Athens provided the navy.

Read to Write Challenge

Students' narratives should describe Leonidas's obedience to the law of Sparta—never surrender on the battlefield.

CHAPTER 7, SECTION 4

Reading Strategy

Citizens: 150,000
Foreigners: 35,000
Enslaved people: 100,000

The Athenian Empire

Evaluating

Student paragraphs will vary. Achievements listed may include: great statesman, led for more than 30 years, reelected again and again, helped Athens dominate the Delian League, included more Athenians in government, culture blossomed under his rule, started a major rebuilding program, supported the arts and philosophy. Students should use specific examples from their lists to support their opinions.

Terms to Know

direct democracy: system of government in which people vote firsthand to decide government matters and make laws and policies; representative democracy: system of government in which people elect a smaller group of people to make laws and decisions on their behalf; philosophers: people who pursue wisdom

Places to Locate

Delos: island serving as headquarters to the Delian League

People to Meet

Pericles: leading figure in Athenian politics after the Persian Wars

Academic Vocabulary

behalf: in the interest of

Sum It Up

In a direct democracy, individuals have a direct voice in their government. In a representative democracy, individuals elect people to make decisions on their behalf.

Daily Life in Athens

Questioning

Student questions will vary. Questions should be based on main ideas in the text, including the population of Athens, slavery, the Athenian economy, the roles of men and women, and Aspasia. Students should supply answers to their questions.

People to Meet

Aspasia: well-educated woman in Athens who shaped the ideas of Plato and was consulted by Athenian leaders

Academic Vocabulary

economy: a system of producing and managing wealth

Sum It Up

Men worked in the morning, then exercised or attended meetings of the assembly. Upper-class men enjoyed all-male gatherings in the evenings. Women took care of household duties and rarely went out. They could leave the house only with a male relative. Women had no political rights. Poor women might also work.

The Peloponnesian War

Predicting

Student predictions will vary. Students should consider the strength of the Spartans as warriors, as well as the learning of the Athenians. Predictions should be supported with facts from the reading.

Academic Vocabulary

framework: structure for supporting something else

Sum It Up

The Spartans tore down the Athenian empire in their victory. The long war weakened all the major Greek city-states. Many were dead or left without farms or jobs. And the Greeks could no longer unite to fight together.

Section Wrap-Up

- Athens dominated the Delian League. The government became more democratic. Culture blossomed. Artists, architects, writers, and philosophers were supported.
- Ultimately, all of Greece was weakened by the long war. Many died, lost farms, and lost jobs. Ultimately the victors, the Spartans, destroyed the Athenian empire. But the city-states rebelled against Spartan control.

Read to Write Challenge

Students' paragraphs should use persuasion in explaining the expectations of male and female citizens to vote and to participate in other ways.

CHAPTER 8, SECTION 1

Reading Strategy

Epic: long poem; tells stories of heroic deeds; based in history
Fable: short story; animals talk and act like humans; points out human flaws and strengths; ends with a moral
Both: Greek stories; taught a lesson

Greek Mythology

Previewing

Student answers will vary. Answers may focus on Greek mythology, gods and goddesses, or the oracle.

Terms to Know

myth: traditional story dealing with gods, goddesses, or heroes; oracle: sacred shrine where a priest or priestess spoke for a god or goddess

Places to Locate

Mount Olympus: the highest mountain in Greece, home to the gods; Delphi: location of the most famous Greek oracle, at the Temple of Apollo

Academic Vocabulary

grant: to give as a favor or privilege, to allow

Sum It Up

The Greeks believed that the gods and goddesses had the power to affect people's lives and to shape events.

Greek Poetry and Fables

Summarizing

Student summaries will vary. Generally, answers should include the following points:
The *Odyssey:* This is the story of the Greek hero Odysseus and his ten-year journey home from the Trojan War.
The *Iliad:* This is the story of the battle for Troy in which the Greeks hide soldiers in a wooden horse to trick the Trojans and win the war.
"The Tortoise and the Hare": This fable tells the story of a tortoise that wins a race against a hare and teaches the moral that "slow and steady wins the race."

Terms to Know

epic: a long Greek poem that told a heroic story; fable: a short story that teaches a lesson

People to Meet

Homer: Greek poet who wrote the *Iliad* and the *Odyssey;* Aesop: Greek slave who wrote fables

Academic Vocabulary

generation: the average period of time between the birth of parents and the birth of their children; tradition: the passing of elements of a culture from one generation to the next

Sum It Up

It is a short tale that teaches a lesson; animals often have human abilities; often funny; points out human flaws and strengths; ends with a moral.

Greek Drama

Connecting

Student answers will vary. Paragraphs should compare the dramas they see with Greek drama. Student answers might reference comedies or tragedies they've seen on stage, film, or television. They should cite differences and similarities, including the use of drama to tell a story with a moral, to make people think as well as laugh, and to entertain.

Terms to Know

drama: a story told by actors who pretend to be characters in the story; tragedy: a drama with a sad ending; comedy: a drama with a happy ending

People to Meet

Sophocles: Greek general and playwright, best known for his tragedies; Euripides: Greek playwright known for his tragedies

Academic Vocabulary

conflict: a state of battle or struggle

Sum It Up

comedies and tragedies

Greek Art and Architecture

Synthesizing

1. reason, moderation, balance, harmony, perfection and beauty
2. in churches and government buildings
3. Student answers should connect Greek ideals in art and architecture with important institutions like the government and church. Answers should reflect how students see these values expressed today.

Sum It Up

temples dedicated to gods and goddesses

Section Wrap-Up

- The Greeks believed that gods and goddesses controlled nature and shaped their lives.
- It showed their ideals of reason, moderation, balance, harmony, perfection and beauty.

Read to Write Challenge

Students' essays should note that theater grew out of festivals given in honor of Dionysus. About 600 B.C., the Ionians began telling stories about the gods, and a chorus chanted and danced to the flute.

CHAPTER 8, SECTION 2

Reading Strategy

Socrates: criticized the Sophists; believed absolute truth exists within everyone; developed the Socratic method

Greek Philosophers

Reviewing

Pythagoras: all relationships can be expressed in numbers; Pythagorean theorem
Socrates: absolute truth exists within everyone; Socratic method
Plato: government should be divided into three groups, ruled by philosopher-kings; men and women should have equal education and employment
Aristotle: "golden mean"; use senses to make observations like a scientist; analyzed governments and decided that the best was a mixture of government by a few and democracy

Terms to Know

philosophy: love or pursuit of wisdom; a system of thought; philosopher: Greek thinker who believed in the power of the human mind; Sophist: professional teacher in ancient Greece; Socratic method: a way of teaching that uses pointed questions to force students to use their reason

Academic Vocabulary

reject: to refuse to accept or believe

Terms to Review

Sample sentences:
A tyrant takes power of the government by force.
In an oligarchy, the government is run by a few people.

Sum It Up

Aristotle thought the best government was a mixture of democracy and government by a few people. Plato did not think the people should have a voice in government at all. He gave all the power to govern to philosopher-kings.

Greek Historians

Skimming

Student answers will vary. Generally, they should identify these ideas:

Herodotus was a Greek historian; he tried to separate fact from legend; some consider him the "father of history"; Thucydides is thought to be the greatest historian in the ancient world; he saw war and politics as activities of human beings.

People to Meet

Herodotus: Greek historian who wrote the history of the Persian Wars; the "father of history"; Thucydides: Greek historian who wrote *History of the Peloponnesian War*

Academic Vocabulary

accurate: correct; containing no error

Sum It Up

He saw war and politics as activities of people, not gods.

Section Wrap-Up

- Sophists: did not believe in gods and goddesses; did not believe in absolute right and wrong; believed truth was relative; Pythagoras: all relationships can be expressed in numbers; Pythagorean theorem; Socrates: absolute truth exists within everyone; Socratic method; Plato: government should be divided into three groups, ruled by philosopher-kings; men and women should have equal education and employment; Aristotle: "golden mean": use senses to make observations like a scientist; believed the best government was a mixture of a few leaders and democracy
- The Greeks were the first to try to explain the past by studying events. Herodotus and Thucydides wrote histories of great wars. They tried to separate fact from legend and use truthful sources.

Read to Write Challenge

For an example of Socratic method dialogue, refer students to Xenophon's *Memorabilia*.

CHAPTER 8, SECTION 3

Reading Strategy

Possible answers include:
Invaded Asia Minor
Won Battle of Granicus
Freed Greek cities in Asia Minor from Persian rule
Captured Syria and Egypt
Built Alexandria
Defeated Persians at Gaugamela
Took rest of Persian Empire
Marched east and entered India

Macedonia Attacks Greece

Predicting

Student answers will vary. They should apply prior learning to make a prediction about the outcome of the Macedonian attack. They should also respond to the actual outcome, reflecting an understanding of the reasons for the Greek's defeat, including: Greece was weak, the population had declined, the war had destroyed many farms, and they fought among themselves.

Places to Locate

Macedonia: kingdom to the north of Greece; Chaeronea: place near Thebes of the Greeks' loss in battle to the Macedonians

People to Meet

Philip II: king of Macedonia who defeated the Greeks

Academic Vocabulary

achieve: to carry out successfully

Sum It Up

He needed to unite the Greek city-states with his own kingdom to defeat the Persian Empire.

Alexander Builds an Empire

Previewing

Student questions will vary. Possible answers include: How did Alexander build his empire? Where did Alexander win battles? What was Alexander's legacy? Why did the empire break apart? Students should use facts from the text to answer their questions.

Terms to Know

legacy: what a person leaves behind after death; Hellenistic Era: period when Greek ideas spread to the peoples of southwest Asia

Places to Locate

Syria: land in Asia Minor captured by Alexander; Alexandria: great city in Egypt built by Alexander

Academic Vocabulary

military: related to the army or war

Terms to Review

Sample sentence: Satraps ruled the states within the Persian Empire.

Sum It Up

Alexander spread Greek and Macedonian rule over a large area. He also spread Greek art, ideas, language, and architecture.

Section Wrap-Up

- He conquered them one city-state at a time. He did this to create a kingdom strong enough to defeat the Persian Empire.
- Alexander spread Greek and Macedonian rule over a large area. He also spread Greek art, ideas, language, and architecture.

Read to Write Challenge

Students' essays should include facts about Alexander in their persuasive summaries.

CHAPTER 8, SECTION 4

Reading Strategy

Answers in ovals should include: philosophy, science and math, and the arts (architecture, sculpture, literature, and theater).

Greek Culture Spreads

Determining the Main Idea

Causes: new Greek cities developed; Alexandria had library and museum; many opportunities to build; leaders supported talented writers
Effects: Philosophers, scientists, poets, and writers flocked to new Greek cities; architects needed to build many new buildings; citizens filled the towns with statues; much literature produced

Sum It Up

Architects, sculptors, writers, philosophers, and scientists all found new opportunities to produce their works as cities grew.

New Philosophy and Science

Responding

Student answers will vary. In general, they should critically examine the two schools of thought, reflect on the nature of happiness, and consider what they believe brings happiness. Epicureans believed that happiness came from seeking out pleasure. Stoics believed that happiness came from following reason and doing your duty.

Terms to Know

Epicureanism: belief that people should seek out pleasure to be happy; Stoicism: belief that people should follow reason and do their duty to find happiness; astronomer: person who studies the stars, planets, and other heavenly bodies; plane geometry: branch of math that shows how points, lines, angles, and surfaces relate to one another; solid geometry: branch of math that studies spheres and cylinders

Academic Vocabulary

goal: a final objective or purpose; lecture: an instructional talk given to a group; major: great in scope or effect; important

Terms to Review

Sample sentences:
Epicurean philosophers believed the people should follow pleasure to be happy.
Stoicism became a very popular philosophy or school of thought.

Sum It Up

Archimedes; he worked on solid geometry and figured out the value of pi.

Section Wrap-Up

- Philosophers, scientists, poets, and writers flocked to Greek cities in the Hellenistic Era. Architects were needed to build many new buildings. Citizens paid for statues and literature.
- Epicurus developed the Epicurean philosophy. Zeno developed the philosophy of Stoicism.

Read to Write Challenge

Students' poems should create a "picture" of Greek accomplishments.

CHAPTER 9, SECTION 1

Reading Strategy

Possible answers include:
Took control of Rome
Changed Rome from a village of straw-roofed huts to a city of wood and brick buildings
Laid out streets, temples, and public buildings
Brought a new style of dress with cloaks and togas
Served as a model for the Roman army

The Origins of Rome

Summarizing

Sample answers:
Romulus and Remus—Twin brothers, Romulus and Remus, were abandoned, rescued by wolves, and raised by a shepherd. As they were building a city, Romulus killed Remus when Remus made fun of the wall he was building. Romulus became the first king of Rome.
The *Aeneid*—The Trojan hero Aeneas united the Trojans and Latins through warfare and marriage. He became the "father" of the Romans.

People to Meet

Latins: the local people who first lived in the area of Rome; Etruscans: group from Etruria who took control of Rome and most of Latium

Places to Locate

Sicily: island near the "toe" of Italy; Apennines: mountain range that runs from the north to the south in Italy; Latium: plain in central Italy where Rome was built; Tiber River: river that connected Rome with the Mediterranean Sea; Etruria: home of the Etruscans, north of Rome

Academic Vocabulary

isolate: to set apart or cut off; capacity: ability to produce or hold

Terms to Review

Sample sentences:
Italy is a long, narrow peninsula with three sides extending into the sea.
The *Aeneid* is an epic, a long, heroic poem.

Sum It Up

The Tiber River gave the Romans a source of water and a way to the sea. It was a good stopping place for people traveling and for merchant ships. It also protected them from pirate raids. Also, the seven hills protected them from attack.

The Birth of a Republic

Reviewing

Excellent soldiers
Fought in legions
Built military settlements and roads
Roman Confederation

Terms to Know

republic: form of government in which the leader is voted into office by citizens; legion: unit or group of soldiers

People to Meet

Tarquins: ruling family under the Etruscans; overthrown by the Romans

Academic Vocabulary

chapter: a distinct period of time; a section of a larger work; status: standing or position as it relates to others

Sum It Up

They created the Roman Confederation. They made them full citizens or allies.

Section Wrap-Up

- The Tiber River gave the Romans a source of water and a way to the sea. It was a good stopping place for people traveling and for merchant ships. It also protected them from pirate raids. Also, the seven hills protected them from attack.
- The Etruscans changed Rome from a village of straw-roofed huts to a city of wood and brick buildings. They laid out streets, temples, and public buildings. Additionally, Romans were excellent soldiers. They built military settlements and roads. They later established the Roman Confederation.

Read to Write Challenge

Students' essays should describe the battle to the death between a noble's slaves at his death banquet. Essays should also mention the underground tombs (catacombs) filled with works of art and treasures ("tombs of gold"), and the cemetery (necropolis) filled with acres of these tombs.

CHAPTER 9, SECTION 2

Reading Strategy

Officials: consuls, praetors, tribunes
Legislative Bodies: Senate, Assembly of Centuries, Council of Plebs

Rome's Government

Questioning

Student questions will vary. In general, they should address the headings, terms, and main ideas within each section, including patricians and plebeians, consuls, veto, praetors, legislative bodies, political reforms, and Cincinnatus.

Terms to Know

patrician: Roman ruling class made up of wealthy landowners; plebeian: Roman social class made up of artisans, shopkeepers, and farmers; consul: top Roman government official; veto: to reject a lawmaker's decision; praetor: Roman official who interpreted the law and acted as a judge; dictator: Roman government official appointed by the Senate to hold absolute power only during times of emergency

Academic Vocabulary

legislate: make law; accommodate: to do a favor or service for; to provide for or allow

Sum It Up

Consuls served short terms and could veto other's decisions.

Roman Law

Connecting

Twelve Tables: all free citizens had the right to be treated equally by the legal system; applied only to Roman citizens
Law of Nations: standards of justice that applied to people everywhere; person innocent until proven guilty; people accused of crimes may defend themselves in front of judge; judge must consider evidence before making decision
Students' paragraphs will vary. Generally, students should recognize many Roman laws in the U.S. system today. They should also consider how their lives might be different without our legal system.

Terms To Review

Sample sentences:
Patricians were Rome's wealthy landowners and ruling class. Most Roman citizens were plebeians—the class of artisans, shopkeepers, and owners of small farms.

Sum It Up

The idea that all people should be treated equally by the legal system is important to protect people from abuses or neglect by the courts.

Rome Expands

Sequencing

_4_ Hannibal attacks Rome.
_5_ Romans lose the Battle of Cannae.
_7_ Scipio's troops defeat the Carthaginians.
_1_ First Punic War begins.
_2_ Rome crushes Carthage's navy off the coast of Sicily.
_3_ Carthage expands its empire into southern Spain.
_9_ Rome gains its first province in Asia.
_6_ Scipio invades Carthage.
_8_ Macedonia comes under Roman rule.

Places to Locate

Carthage: state on the coast of North Africa; enemy of war in the Punic Wars; Cannae: location of battle lost by the Romans in 216 B.C.; Zama: location of battle where Scipio's troops defeated the Carthaginians

People to Meet

Hannibal: greatest general from Carthage; fought in the Second Punic War; Scipio: Roman general who defeated the Carthaginians

Academic Vocabulary

challenge: a test of ability

Sum It Up

They burned Carthage, took 50,000 slaves, and spread salt on the earth so no more crops would grow.

Section Wrap-Up

- The republic included consuls, praetors, the Senate, and the Assembly of Centuries. The government changed to give representation to plebeians. They set up the Council of Plebs, elected tribunes, and won the right to veto. They also gained the power to pass laws for all Romans.
- Rome battled and defeated Carthage in the First, Second, and Third Punic Wars. Rome moved on to capture Macedonia and part of Asia.

Read to Write Challenge

Students' paragraphs should describe King Pyrrhus's victories over the Romans in 280 and 279 B.C. Paragraphs should also include the meaning of "Pyrrhic victory," or a victory obtained at an incredible cost.

CHAPTER 9, SECTION 3

Reading Strategy

Student answers will vary. Generally, answers should reflect the following points.
Main Idea: The Roman Republic Falls
Supporting Ideas:

Enslaved labor hurts the republic; farmers lose land and jobs; politics become weak and corrupt; politicians refuse to make needed reforms; powerful generals take control to get land

Republic is weakened by fighting; Caesar takes Rome and implements reform but is killed; Octavian and Antony fight for power

Octavian makes himself an emperor; Octavian defeats Antony and establishes a limited republic based on the ideas of Cicero

Trouble in the Republic

Monitoring Comprehension

Possible answers include: the rich people held the power; rich pushed the small farmers off their land; enslaved labor displaced

small farmers; generals gain power by promising land to hired soldiers

Terms to Know

latifundia: large farming estates

Academic Vocabulary

despite: in spite of; estate: a large piece of land or property

Sum It Up

He moved it from an army of citizen volunteers to paid professional soldiers.

Julius Caesar

Drawing Conclusions

Destroyed Pompey's army to become dictator of Rome
Filled Senate with loyal people
Granted citizenship to people living in territories outside the peninsula
Started new colonies to provide land for the landless
Created work for the jobless
Ordered landowners to hire more free workers
Created a new 12-month calendar
Student conclusions will vary. Students should be able to support their conclusion using facts from their reading.

Terms to Know

triumvirate: a political alliance of three people

Places to Locate

Rubicon: small river crossed by Caesar on his conquest to capture Rome; marks Caesar's decision to start a civil war

Sum It Up

They feared he wanted to be king.

Rome Becomes an Empire

Connecting

Argued against dictators
Called for representative government with limited powers
Student paragraphs will vary. Generally, students should connect Cicero's ideas about government to their government today. They should also consider how their lives might be different without these ideas.

Places to Locate

Actium: location of Octavian's victory in battle against Antony and Cleopatra

People to Meet

Octavian: member of Second Triumvirate who defeated Antony to become emperor; Antony: member of Second Triumvirate; defeated by Octavian; Cicero: Roman political leader, writer, and speaker; called for representative government; Augustus: "the revered or majestic one"; title taken by Octavian

Academic Vocabulary

sole: the only one, single; foundation: the base on which something stands

Sum It Up

Octavian's rule ended the Roman Republic and laid the foundation for the Roman Empire.

Section Wrap-Up

- He fought a civil war for control. He initiated many reforms but took power for life. He was killed because people feared his power. His death plunged the country back into civil war.
- When Octavian defeated Antony, he felt the republic was too weak to solve Rome's problems. So he kept the real power as ruler. He, in effect, made himself an emperor.

Read to Write Challenge

Students' paragraphs should reflect persuasive techniques—logic, emotion, counterarguments, and so on.

CHAPTER 9, SECTION 4

Reading Strategy

Possible answers include:
Change: Built a permanent, professional army
Effect: Strength and safety; new territories
Change: Rebuilt Rome
Effect: Arts flourished
Change: Imported grain to feed the poor
Effect: People more loyal
Change: Appointed governors
Effect: Better government for huge population
Change: Roman tax system
Effect: Made the system more fair
Change: Reformed legal system
Effect: Laws of Rome applied to everyone

The Emperor Augustus

Drawing Conclusions

Student answers will vary. Students should consider the reforms made by Augustus and the strength of the military. Students should also consider the fact that the emperor did not rule alone. He held most of the power, but the Senate was still active.

Terms to Know

Pax Romana: "Roman Peace"; the long period of peace that began with Augustus and lasted until A.D. 180

People to Meet

Caligula: one of the Julio-Claudian emperors; cruel and mentally ill; Nero: one of the Julio-Claudian emperors; very cruel

Academic Vocabulary

successor: person who succeeds or follows another; commit: to do or perform

Sum It Up

He built a permanent, professional army along with a special unit called the Praetorian Guard.

Unity and Prosperity

Outlining

I. Unity and Prosperity
  A. Rome passed through a period of disorder after Nero committed suicide.
  B. Titus and Domitian oversaw a period of growth and wealth.

II. The "Good Emperors"
  A. Nerva, Trajan, Hadrian, Antoninus Pius, and Marcus Aurelius ruled as the "good emperors."
  B. These emperors did much to help ordinary people, including the poor and orphans.

III. A Unified Empire
  A. The empire grew until it was too big to manage, and Hadrian pulled back the boundaries.
  B. The Roman Empire was one of the greatest empires in history in the A.D. 100s.

IV. A Booming Economy
  A. Most people in the empire made a living from the land.
  B. Industry and trade were also an important part of the economy.

V. Roads and Money
  A. Rome's system of roads grew during the *Pax Romana.*
  B. Rome's trade was helped by a common currency and a system of weights and measures.

VI. Ongoing Inequality
  A. Many people in Rome remained poor, and many remained enslaved.

Terms to Know

aqueduct: channel made to carry water long distances; currency: system of money

Places to Locate

Rhine River: part of empire's eastern boundary set by Hadrian; Danube River: part of empire's eastern boundary set by Hadrian; Puteoli: large port city on the Bay of Naples; Ostia: large port city at the mouth of the Tiber

Academic Vocabulary

capable: having the ability to do a task

Sum It Up

Nerva, Trajan, Hadrian, Antoninus Pius, and Marcus Aurelius ruled as the "good emperors." Trajan gave money to help poor parents raise and educate their children. Hadrian made Roman law easier to understand and apply. Antoninus Pius passed laws to help orphans. All supported public building projects.

Section Wrap-Up

• Augustus made Rome strong. He built a permanent, professional army, rebuilt Rome, imported grain to feed the poor, appointed governors, established a fair tax system, and reformed the legal system.
• Military strength, legal and social reforms, a system of roads, aqueducts, ports, and

common currency made the empire rich and prosperous.

Read to Write Challenge

Students' biographical sketches should include birth and death dates, major accomplishments or major failures, and how the emperor died.

CHAPTER 10, SECTION 1

Reading Strategy

Rich: large, comfortable houses; fine furniture; gardens; villas; tutors
Poor: Overcrowded wood and stone apartment buildings; limited space; poorly built, dangerous housing; free grain; no schooling
Both: chariot races and gladiator contests; paterfamilias

Roman Culture

Synthesizing

Student answers will vary. Students should use the accounts of Livy and Tacitus as models. They should apply learning from their current reading, previous chapters, and outside research to develop their own accounts of Roman history.

Terms to Know

vault: a curved ceiling built with rows of arches; satire: a work of literature that pokes fun at human weaknesses; ode: a poem that expresses strong emotions about life; anatomy: the study of the human body

People to Meet

Virgil: Roman writer; author of the *Aeneid;* Horace: Roman poet; wrote satires and odes; Galen: Greek doctor who studied anatomy and brought many medical ideas to Rome; Ptolemy: Scientist of the Roman Empire who studied the sky, planets, and stars; he placed Earth at the center of the universe

Academic Vocabulary

technique: the specific way a task is accomplished or handled

Terms to Review

Sample sentence: Greek myths tell stories about the gods.

Sum It Up

They used arches, domes, and concrete.

Daily Life in Rome

Inferring

Students should explore the need to keep the people happy. They should look at the reasons Romans may have rioted, including crowded, noisy, and dirty living conditions, crime, poverty, high rents, poorly constructed buildings, danger from fire, and the extreme differences between the lives of the rich and the lives of the poor.

Terms to Know

Forum: the open space at the center of Roman cities that served as a marketplace

and public square; gladiator: a person who fought animals or another gladiator for entertainment; paterfamilias: "father of the family;" Roman fathers who exercised complete control over their families; rhetoric: public speaking

People to Meet

Spartacus: gladiator who led a slave revolt in 73 B.C.

Academic Vocabulary

constant: unchanging; state of ongoing possibility

Sum It Up

Upper-class women had much independence. They could own land, run businesses, and sell property. They had slaves to do the housework. They had time to study, and they could go to the theater.

Section Wrap-Up

• The Romans copied Greek art, architecture, and literature. They also developed their own ideas. They made their art more realistic. They added their own ideas to architecture and developed their own great works of literature. They made important advances in engineering, building a huge system of roads and supplying cities with fresh water.
• The rich lived well. The poor had little. All people enjoyed the chariot races and gladiator events. The father ruled the family. Wealthy women enjoyed many freedoms. Women with less money spent more of their time working. Slavery was common. The people worshiped Roman gods and goddesses.

Read to Write Challenge

Students' essays should include a description of the burial of Pompeii as well as the art, architecture, and other items of daily life that were excavated.

CHAPTER 10, SECTION 2

Reading Strategy

Answers include:
  Weak government, social problems, and economic problems
  Diocletian divides the empire into four parts
  Constantine moves the capital
  The empire splits into the Western and Eastern Roman Empires
  Attacks threaten the empire, and territory is slowly lost

The Decline of Rome

Summarizing

Diocletian: divided the empire into four parts; issued rules that set prices and wages; ordered workers to remain at the same jobs until they died
Constantine: sons of workers had to follow their fathers' trades; sons of farmers had to

work their fathers' land; sons of soldiers had to serve in the army; moved the capital

Terms to Know

inflation: rapidly increasing prices; happens when money loses its value; barter: to trade goods without using money; reform: political change to make things better

Places to Locate

Constantinople: the Greek city named by Constantine as the new capital of the empire

Academic Vocabulary

authority: power to make others obey or enforce laws

Sum It Up

He divided the empire into four parts; issued rules that set prices and wages; ordered workers to remain at the same jobs until they died.

Rome Falls

Scanning

1. It was split into two separate empires.
2. They were in search of warmer climates and better grazing land. They were also drawn by Rome's wealth and culture. Many were fleeing the Huns.
3. The Visigoths defeated Roman legions. Rome was forced to surrender land.
4. He was the Visigoth leader who captured Rome.
5. He was the Germanic general who took control of Rome for almost 15 years.

People to Meet

Theodosius: Roman emperor who divided the empire into the Western and Eastern Empires

Sum It Up

When the German general Odoacer took control of Rome, overthrowing the western emperor

The Legacy of Rome

Reviewing

Government: Ideas that all people are equal, judges are fair, and a person is innocent until proven guilty; belief that a republic is the best form of government; ideals of citizenship
Culture: alphabet and Latin language; works of Roman writers; use of concrete; architecture
Religion: spread of Christianity

Academic Vocabulary

expand: to make bigger; to increase in size

Terms to Review

Sample sentence: The Roman idea of a republic made up of equal citizens helped shape the American government.

Sum It Up

government, law, citizenship, culture, language, literature, architecture, and religion

Section Wrap-Up

- Social and economic problems, including inflation, weakened the empire. Reforms

were not effective, and Diocletian divided the empire into four parts. Constantine moved the capital. Finally, the empire split into the Western and Eastern Roman Empires.
- Roman ideas have affected out government, law, citizenship, culture, language, literature, architecture, and religion.

Read to Write Challenge

Students' lists will vary but could include *ante meridiem* (A.M.) and *post meridiem* (P.M.), *exit, ad hoc, alumni, per capita,* and so on. The categorization of species includes Latin names for phylum, class, order, family, genus, and species.

CHAPTER 10, SECTION 3

Reading Strategy

Possible answers include:
Causes: Empire's laws were disorganized and too difficult to understand
Effect: Simplified the code and made it easier to understand; has influenced the laws of almost every country in Europe

The Rise of the Byzantines

Previewing

Student answers will vary. Answers may focus on Constantine, the location of Constantinople, or the influence of Greek culture.

Places to Locate

Black Sea: waterway that bordered Constantinople; Aegean Sea: waterway that bordered Constantinople

Terms to Review

Sample sentence: Constantinople was located on a peninsula, protected by water on three sides.

Sum It Up

More Byzantines spoke Greek and honored their Greek past. The ideas of non-Greek peoples also influenced Byzantine culture.

Emperor Justinian

Determining the Main Idea

Sample answer: The policies and reforms of Emperor Justinian and Empress Theodora helped make the Byzantine Empire strong.

People to Meet

Justinian: emperor of the Byzantine Empire who ruled from A.D. 527 to A.D. 565; created the Justinian Code; Theodora: wife of Justinian; helped save Justinian's throne; Belisarius: general who strengthened and led the Byzantine army; Tribonian: legal scholar who headed the reform of the law code leading to the Justinian Code

Academic Vocabulary

income: money received for work completed; rely: to depend on

Sum It Up

He conquered most of Italy and northern Africa and defeated the Persians in the east. He also reformed the law code and developed the Justinian Code.

Byzantine Civilization

Outlining

I. The Importance of Trade
   A. The Byzantine Empire was the center of trade between Europe and Asia.
   B. Trade made the empire very rich.
II. Byzantine Art and Architecture
   A. Byzantine emperors supported artists and architects.
   B. One of Justinian's greatest achievements was building Hagia Sophia.
III. Byzantine Women
   A. The family was the center of social life for most Byzantines.
   B. Byzantine women gained some important rights thanks to Empress Theodora.
IV. Byzantine Education
   A. Learning was highly respected in Byzantine culture.
   B. Most Byzantine authors wrote about religion.

Terms to Know

mosaic: pictures made from many bits of colored glass or stone; saint: Christian holy people; regent: a person who stands in for a ruler who is too young or too ill to govern

Academic Vocabulary

enormous: very large; huge

Terms to Review

Sample sentence: Groups of people traveled together in caravans to carry their spices, gems, and cloth to trade.

Sum It Up

Hagia Sophia

Section Wrap-Up

- Justinian made the army stronger and reformed the law. He produced the Justinian Code.
- The Byzantines valued arts and architecture, learning and education, and religion.

Read to Write Challenge

The four parts to the Code include the *Digest*—decisions of the great Roman jurists; the *Institutes*—a textbook for law students; the *Novels*—the actual edicts issued by Justinian; and the *Codex*—a collection of statutes and principles.

CHAPTER 11, SECTION 1

Reading Strategy

Worship; Teaching and Study; Prayer

The Jews and the Romans

Connecting

Student answers will vary. Students should consider their responses to authority. Do they tend to rebel? Do they tend to try to work together? Are their responses different depending on the person and how they approach the situation? Ask students to consider how they think they might have responded to the Romans as a Jew.

Places to Locate

Jerusalem: capital of Israel; Judaea: Roman name for Judah

Sum It Up

The Romans forced all Jews to leave Jerusalem and banned them from returning.

The Life of Jesus

Responding

Student responses will vary. Students should relate that the Samaritan, a person who was looked down upon, helped when no one else would. Jesus taught in parables because people responded to stories that related experiences from everyday life.

Terms to Know

messiah: a savior or someone who rescues another from harm; disciple: a person who follows the teachings of another; parable: a story that teaches a lesson using everyday events; resurrection: act of rising from the dead or coming back to life

Places to Locate

Jerusalem: capital of Israel; Nazareth: home of Jesus; Galilee: region just north of Judaea where Jesus preached

Academic Vocabulary

decade: period of time equal to ten years

Sum It Up

People should turn from their sins; having a relationship with God is more important than following religious law; love God with all your heart, and love your neighbor as yourself.

The First Christians

Predicting

Headings and details may vary. Samples include:

Early Christians: Jesus' disciples spread his teachings; people who accepted Jesus and his teachings were called Christians; early churches met for worship and teaching in people's homes; they prayed, worshiped, and shared a meal like the Last Supper

Peter and Paul: early Christian apostles; Peter was one of Jesus' 12 disciples; he helped set up the church in Rome; Paul persecuted Christians; on the road to Damascus, Paul saw a light and became a Christian; he spent the rest of his life spreading Jesus' message; he started many churches

Christian Beliefs: Jesus was the Son of God; people are saved from sin by accepting Jesus; after death, they join God in everlasting life; the God of Israel and the Hebrew Bible; the Trinity

Terms to Know

apostle: early Christian leaders who started new churches and taught Jesus' message; salvation: being delivered or saved from sin, destruction, or evil

Academic Vocabulary

reside: to live in a place permanently

Sum It Up

Peter was an apostle. He was a fisher who became one of the 12 disciples. He helped set up the church in Rome.

Paul was an educated man who persecuted Christians. He saw a great light and heard Jesus' voice on the road to Damascus. He became a Christian and an apostle. He started many churches.

Section Wrap-Up

- He taught that God was coming soon to rule the world; people should turn from their sins; having a relationship with God is more important than following religious law; love and forgive from the heart; love God with all your heart, and love your neighbor as yourself.
- People responded differently to Jesus. Some followed him. Some feared him. Others disagreed with him. Still others wanted to kill him. Ultimately, leaders in Jerusalem arrested and crucified him.

Read to Write Challenge

Students' narratives should describe the Good Samaritan parable in a modern setting.

CHAPTER 11, SECTION 2

Reading Strategy

Peace and order of Rome
Message gave meaning to people's lives
Ideas of Christianity were familiar
Gave people the chance to be part of a caring group

A Growing Faith

Inferring

Student answers should reflect the differences between Christian beliefs and practices and Roman law and practices. Christians refused to honor the emperor as god. They would have viewed government and society as corrupt, so they would have refused to participate in social or political activities that went against their beliefs.

Terms to Know

persecute: to treat someone badly; martyr: someone who is willing to die instead of giving up their beliefs

People to Meet

Constantine: Roman general who became emperor in A.D. 312; accepted Christianity; Helena: Constantine's mother; helped build churches in Rome and Jerusalem; Theodosius: emperor after Constantine who made Christianity the official religion of Rome

Academic Vocabulary

establish: to set up; found; issue: to give out; to distribute

Sum It Up

They would not honor the emperor as a god. They criticized Roman festivals and games. They also refused to serve in the army or hold public office.

The Early Church

Scanning

Top box: pope
#2 box: patriarchs
#3 box: archbishops
#4 box: bishops
#5 box: priests

Terms to Know

hierarchy: a group of people with different levels of power or authority; clergy: leaders of the church; laity: regular church members; doctrine: official church teaching; gospel: one of the first four books of the New Testament: Matthew, Mark, Luke, and John; pope: bishop of Rome, head of the church

Academic Vocabulary

unify: to bring together, to unite as one

Sum It Up

The gospels are four accounts of Jesus' life written by early followers named Matthew, Mark, Luke, and John. They are written records of Jesus' life and form part of the New Testament.

Section Wrap-Up

- Constantine became a Christian after seeing a vision. He made Christianity legal. Then his successor, Theodosius, made Christianity Rome's official religion.
- It was organized in a hierarchy. Levels included the pope at the top, followed by patriarchs, archbishops, bishops, priests, and then the laity.

Read to Write Challenge

Students' narratives should include information about Perpetua's early aristocratic life as well as her death by wild beasts in the arena at Carthage in A.D. 203.

CHAPTER 11, SECTION 3

Reading Strategy

Eastern Europe: Paula, Cyril
Britain/Ireland: Patrick, Pope Gregory I

The Byzantine Church

Summarizing

Sample answers:

The pope opposed the Byzantine emperor's decision to remove icons from the churches.

Only the Roman church recognized the pope as head of church, with both spiritual and political power.

The churches refused to help each other when attacked.

The pope made Charlemagne emperor, but the Byzantines recognized their own emperor.

Terms to Know

icon: pictures or images of Jesus, Mary (the mother of Jesus), and the saints, or Christian holy people; iconoclast: someone who attacks traditional beliefs or institutions; excommunicate: to say that a person or group no longer belongs to the church; schism: a separation, or split

People to Meet

Charlemagne: Frankish king made emperor by the pope in A.D. 800

Places to Locate

Byzantine Empire: name for the Roman Empire as it developed in Eastern Europe

Academic Vocabulary

survive: to continue to live or exist

Sum It Up

Church and government worked together closely. The Byzantines believed their emperor represented Jesus Christ on Earth. The emperor chose the leading church official. The emperor was in control, and the church leaders respected his wishes.

Christian Ideas Spread

Sequencing

 __4__ Patrick brings Christianity to Ireland.

 __3__ Cyril invents a new Slavic alphabet.

 __2__ Paula builds churches, a hospital, and a convent in Palestine.

 __1__ Monks band together into the first monasteries.

 __5__ Pope Gregory I sends monks to take Christianity to England.

Terms to Know

monastery: a place where men called monks live together in a religious community; missionary: person who teaches his or her religion to those who do not believe

People to Meet

Cyril: Byzantine missionary who invented a Slavic alphabet; Patrick: priest who brought Christianity to Ireland

Places to Locate

Britain: island where Christian missionaries traveled seeking converts; Ireland: island where Christian missionaries traveled seeking converts

Sum It Up

Basil was a bishop who drew up a list of rules for monks and nuns. The Basilian Rule became the model for Eastern Orthodox religious life. Benedict was an Italian monk who drew up a set of rules for monks and nuns. The Benedictine Rule became the model for the West.

Section Wrap-Up

* Church and government worked together closely. The Byzantines believed their emperor represented Jesus Christ on Earth. The emperor chose the leading church official. The emperor was in control, and the church leaders respected his wishes.

* Monks and nuns served as missionaries. Missionaries traveled to other countries to spread their faith. Cyril and Methodius carried the message to the Slavs. Patrick brought Christianity to Ireland. And other missionaries carried the message to Britain and Ireland.

Read to Write Challenge

Students' essays should incorporate the following activities performed by monks each day:

12:00 A.M.—Matins: Half-hour worship service

6:00 A.M.—Prime: Half-hour worship followed by breakfast and work

9:00 A.M.—Mass: Worship service followed by community meeting

11:00 A.M.—High Mass: Worship service followed by meal, rest, and reading time

2:00 P.M.—Nones: Half-hour worship service followed by work

4:00 P.M.—Vespers: Half-hour worship service followed by work

7:00 P.M.—Compline: Evening prayer in the church